Contents

Welcome!

Welcome to the Alkaline Diet Recipe Book Volume II!

Wow - here we are with another recipe book! So much has happened since I first released the original recipe book, I'm not sure quite where to start.

Since that book was released in 2009 I have been on such an amazing journey. I have learned so much, developed so many new skills and strategies and have been incredibly fortunate to have been able to reach so many more people, more than ever before, and I feel truly fortunate to be able to share this with you. The first recipe book sold like wildfire and the reviews and testimonials I received were amazing - they truly blew me away.

This new recipe book has been a labour of love, just like the first volume. But I know just how important it is and how much it is going to help you on your alkaline journey. Having delicious, easy to cook alkaline meals is one of the most, if not the most, important parts of successfully and enjoyably living alkaline and staying alkaline for life. And now you have just given yourself that tool! I hope you love the recipes in this book as much as I have loved creating them!

It's been a long journey, but I'm truly excited to have the opportunity to share my second recipe book with you and help play a part in your health journey.

My Big Why

I am absolutely, passionately driven to help you get the health, vitality, body and energy of your dreams. It truly is my number one passion.

I truly believe that everything we want to achieve in life starts with our health at the core. I truly believe that when you are healthy and vibrant, every other area of your life falls into place. You're more positive when you're healthy. You wake up earlier and have the energy to go to bed later. You find more time to work on your goals, more time to exercise, more time to spend with your kids and loved ones, more time to make a difference. When you are healthy you follow your dreams, you don't put things off until tomorrow, you take action, you challenge yourself, you respect yourself and you strive to keep on improving.

When you're healthy, your whole life improves - things just click into place.

This is why 'my big why' in life, my big passion, my big purpose is to support you to smash through your health goals and get the health, body and life you've always dreamed of.

My big why is to give you everything you need to get to the health, energy, body and life of your dreams. That's why I'm here. I'm here to help you.

It's what's driven me to do this for so long! Since I started in 2004 I've written over 550 alkaline diet guides and articles, over 150 free alkaline diet recipes, interviewed dozens of amazing health experts such as Dr Young, Joseph McClendon and more and answered over 50,000 questions, via email, personally - all totally for free - to help get you to your health goals.

And over the past nine years of doing this much research, writing and teaching - and of course living it myself - I've developed a knack for getting people alkaline, keeping them alkaline and showing them how to enjoy the process. Let's be totally honest here, I'm not a Doctor and I don't have a PhD in biology or physiology.

But what I do have is over nine years of experience specifically targeted at getting people just like you - alkaline for life. I know how to take you from wherever you are now, to living alkaline and absolutely nailing your health goals quickly and easily and enjoyably. It's like my super-power - I am 'Get People Alkaline While Helping Them Enjoy It' Man.

Or probably something a bit more catchy.

But in all seriousness - it's my passion, my purpose and something I've become very very good at. If you want to get alkaline, I know I can get you there.

So stick with me, keep in touch with me, connect with me and contact me whenever you like! I openly invite you to!

Ross Bridgeford

ross@liveenergized.com

2

The **Alkaline** Diet

The alkaline diet is a very, very simple and straightforward approach to health, but is backed by extensive science.

I've been working with, researching, coaching, living and writing about the alkaline diet for a long time, and I've been asked to explain it hundreds, if not thousands of times!

It is something I used to struggle to explain concisely because you can go into so much depth on it! But I have now settled for a simple explanation and that's what I'm going to give you now!

Our body is designed to be alkaline. The pH of most of our important cellular and other fluids such as our blood is designed to be at a pH of 7.365, which is slightly alkaline. In just the same way that our body will do whatever it takes to regulate our temperature to stay within a very tight range, it does the same for the pH of our fluids. And while our body does create acids naturally through our bodily functions, we have a small alkaline buffering system that naturally keeps us alkaline.

Your body HAS to keep the pH of your blood, cells and other fluids at just slightly alkaline (pH 7.365) and it will do ANYTHING it has to in order to maintain this pH balance. To do this, your body calls upon its store of alkaline buffers, which it draws upon to neutralize the acids we ingest or create through bodily processes. This store of buffers is very easily depleted because most of us eat and drink such strong acids.

To put this in context, the pH scale is logarithmic – so pH 6 is 10x more acidic than pH 7, meaning pH 5 is 100x times more acidic than pH 7 and pH 4 is 1000x more acidic. Cola has a pH of between 2 and 3. So you can see how a diet filled with meats, dairy, fizzy drinks, alcohol etc would quickly deplete these buffers.

And when we deplete these buffers and still ingest more acids… what happens?

The body is forced into drawing upon the alkaline minerals it has to buffer which causes havoc in the body – for instance, if the body is constantly drawing calcium to neutralise the acids we consume then the symptoms of osteoporosis emerge (hence the recent research articles linking cola consumption with osteoporosis).

However, as we have evolved and our diets and lifestyles have changed over the last century or so we have dramatically increased the amount of acidity in our lives. Diet, stress, emotions and no exercise contribute, in their own ways to the increased acidity in our body.

It will be no surprise to you to learn that the most acidic foods are sugar, trans-fats, yeasts, dairy, simple carbs, alcohol, refined foods etc. These acids manifest in our diets as colas & fizzy drinks, pizza, chips, cakes, biscuits, microwave meals, crisps, breads, caffeine, cheese, fatty meats, ice cream, smoking, beers, wines, condiments, milky drinks, cream etc. all the foods you already know are not good for you.

I'm sure you can guess that the foods that are alkaline to the body are therefore…wait for it…fresh vegetables, salads, leafy greens, omega oils, nuts, seeds, pulses, whole grains. These are fresh foods, raw foods, whole foods, foods with a high-water content and nutritional value.

It makes this diet pretty easy to understand and pretty easy to follow. I think most people, if given a list of foods could put them into the acid or alkaline group 8 times out of 10.

So what makes a food acid or alkaline? There are a few things, but the most important rules are:

1   If a food is high in alkaline minerals including magnesium, potassium, calcium or sodium it is likely to be alkaline to the body.

2   BUT – regardless of its alkaline mineral content, if it contains any of the following then it will be acidifying:
- Sugar (article about sugar)
- Yeast
- Is fermented (like soy sauce)
- Contains fungi (like mushrooms)
- Is refined/microwaved/processed

So this explains the anomalies. Fruit for instance is generally, unfortunately, acidifying due to it's high sugar content. Bananas for example are very high in potassium, but are around 25% sugar. The only exceptions are tomatoes, avocados, lemons & limes (great for dressings and flavourings), grapefruit and watermelon (to some degree) which are alkaline because they are so low in sugar.

Sugar is such an issue because the blood deviates from this pH level of 7.365 then it causes major stress to the rest of the body. The body has to maintain this pH level and it will go to extreme measures and sacrifice everything else to make sure it stays there.

It compounds the longer it goes on.

Emotions, stress and a lack of exercise all contribute to this and can have twice as much of an effect on our blood and health as any food can, so these all play a part.

Exercise is obviously essential because it pumps our blood and lymph around the body to remove wastes and helps to deliver oxygen to cells for necessary functioning.

So, there you have it, that was my slightly expanded version!

The Simple Version

Here is my more simple version of what the alkaline diet is and why it works so well!

Forget science, forget chemistry and biology for a second. Let me explain the alkaline approach to health in really simple terms. I am not a scientist, so this is how I figured it out in a way it would work for me and make sense in my mind, and this explanation has made sense to everyone else I've spoken to about it!

Here goes… The alkaline diet is an approach to health and life that recommends making 70-80% of your food and drink consumption those foods and drinks that have an alkaline effect on the body.

This still leaves room for non-alkaline foods, and still leaves room for flexibility - you're not striving for perfection. The reason why it makes sense is because if you look at the list of foods that are alkaline they are all the foods you know are good for you: vegetables, salads, leafy greens, high-water content foods - foods like spinach, broccoli, carrots, lettuce, cucumber, nuts, seeds, oily fish, low-sugar fruits and more.

Now, there are LOADS more alkaline foods than that, but this gives you the picture. All the healthiest foods you could possibly think of all have an alkaline effect on the body.

Now, let's look at the acidic-forming foods. Can you guess what they might be? Surprise, surprise it's sugar, chocolate, pizza, chips, fried foods, trans fats, junk food, takeaways, dairy, wheats, yeasts, gluten-containing foods, alcohol, refined foods and so on.

Is this starting to sound like a sensible, natural way to go?

So to live alkaline you need to simply follow a set of simple rules:

1 Focus 70-80% of your food consumption on alkaline-forming foods such as vegetables, salads, low-sugar fruits, oily fish, nuts and seeds, omega oils and more.

2 Try to minimise the consumption of acid-forming foods such as sugar, refined foods, junk foods, chocolate, sweets, baked goods, pizzas, chips, burgers, trans fats, partially hydrogenated fats, alcohol, soda and so on.

3 Ensure you get at least 2-3 litres of good quality, clean, preferably alkaline water each day

4 Undertake varied, moderate exercise regularly

5 Try to live without stress & negativity

I am pretty sure that there is not one single Doctor, nutritionist or health expert anywhere in the world that would disagree with the above.

It makes it pretty simple when you stick to these easy to understand rules!

Top Four Alkaline Questions

I've been researching, writing, living, teaching and coaching the alkaline diet for over nine years now and have helped tens of thousands of people to get alkaline and get the health and body of their dreams.

I have answered over 50,000 questions from people via email - but these four questions come up over and over again! So I wanted to address them for you here. The fifth question that comes up is usually "What can I eat?" but I would like to think having my Recipe Book will answer that one for you!

1 Everyone KNOWS lemons are acidic. Why do you recommend them?

This is a quite common question, so I'm getting quite good at answering it in a nice and simple way!

It is basically about what effect the food has on the body once consumed rather than it's acidity or alkalinity in its natural state. Lemons, while containing citric acid have a very high content of the strongly alkaline minerals potassium, magnesium and sodium. These minerals have a very alkalising effect on the body.

The reason this doesn't work with oranges is because the sugar content of the orange is so high that cancels out the alkalising minerals and leads it to have a very acidifying effect on the body.

That is the same for almost all fruits (unfortunately).

Which brings us onto…

2 Can I eat fruit?

Unfortunately, the answer to this one is, generally, no. Fruits should be treated as a treat, or 'emergency food'. Better than a chocolate bar, yes, but the sugar content of fruit makes it actually quite acidifying. You really need to avoid all sugar, whether it is fructose, sucrose, glucose (anything ending in -ose). They all have the same effect on the body – sugar is sugar is sugar, no matter where you get it from and fruit is absolutely packed with it.

While I understand that fruit also contains fibre, vitamins, phytonutrients etc. the sheer amount of sugar that fruit contains means that this not a worthwhile trade off.

The Problem with Sugar
(and a quick crash course on why an acidic lifestyle is so bad)

In the same way that our body will do whatever it has to in order to maintain a temperature of 37 degrees, it will go to similar lengths to maintain a pH level of 7.365 for our internal cells, particularly the blood.

The modern Western diet of meats, dairy, fizzy drinks, chips, chocolate, candy, alcohol, coffee, pizza, pasta, bread etc has a massively acidic effect on the body. Such an acidic lifestyle puts incredible stress and strain on the body as it has to constantly fire-fight to keep this pH level of 7.365.

This not only takes up a MASSIVE amount of our energy (remember how you feel after Christmas dinner or a huge takeaway meal?) but it also uses up the alkaline minerals (buffers) in our body including calcium, potassium, magnesium and sodium. This in turn leads to so many health issues it is unreal.

These acid-forming foods and drinks also lead to the creation of yeasts, bacteria and mold in our blood. In addition, the acids that are created and consumed in our modern lifestyle also ferment the blood and create harmful by-products, toxins and alcohols, which then further destroy our internal environment.

With more acid, more toxins are created, the pH is lowered, the bacteria and yeast grows, becomes mold, and a vicious cycle begins.

And what's more – these harmful bacteria, yeast and mold actually feed off the nutrients you consume! But that is not all! The waste products they leave behind also act as their food, meaning that rapid multiplication takes place!

So when we consume sugar it sends our body into turmoil. Consuming sugar is like throwing petrol onto a fire. It rapidly fuels this cycle, compounding the problem and placing an insane amount of stress on the body.

I've written about this before and a number of questions and concerns often arise, but the question that comes up most frequently is this:

But sugar from fruit is different isn't it? Fructose is ok, right?

NOPE.

Sugar is sugar is sugar. It doesn't matter where it comes from, it still wreaks havoc with the acid/alkaline balance of the body. Whether it is from fructose, sucrose, an apple, honey or a piece of chocolate cake, the sugar still has the same devastating effect. How quickly or slowly the body metabolises different sugars may have an effect on your energy levels (in terms of how quickly the peaks and troughs will follow one another) but makes no difference to the fact that the sugar ferments and fuels these harmful microforms in exactly the same way.

So stop eating fruit in excess! It is plain to see that sugar is incredibly harmful, and fruit is packed full of it. And as for fruit juice? Fresh or not, fruit juice is simply highly concentrated fruit! But without the fibre! It is the same problem multiplied by twenty.

DO NOT DRINK FRUIT JUICE!

Sure, if it is the choice between an apple and a Mars bar then go for the apple, because you're at least getting some goodness. But better still, give yourself better choices so you don't have to go for the lesser of two evils! (Wow, five years ago I never would have thought I would be calling fruit 'evil'!)

Is any fruit OK?

Yes! There are a handful of low-sugar fruits that are great for you! Tomato, avocado, lemon, lime, pomegranate, watermelon and grapefruit are all alkalising and full of goodness. The reason lemons and limes have an alkalising effect is because they are not only high water content and low sugar content, but they also contain high amounts of alkaline minerals (potassium in particular).

7

3   Why are the lists of alkaline/acid foods different?

I know it is quite confusing to see such differences in the charts. This amount of conflicting information is the main reason I set up energiseforlife.com and I believe our chart (based on the research of the Alkaline Diet pioneer, Dr Young) is the most accurate.

The reason that other charts show such disparity is because they base their classifications on the readings for the Potential Renal Acid Load research (PRAL). This is not an accurate source for this purpose. The reason for this is, to test for PRAL they basically burn the food at an extreme temperature and then take a read of the 'ash' that is left behind and what it's pH is.

While this does give a read of its alkalinity from the mineral content of the food, this is only half the picture. By burning it at such a high temperature they also burn away all of the most acid-causing content of the food, namely sugar. That is why on some charts high sugar fruits are listed as alkaline. Bananas for instance are high in the alkaline mineral potassium, BUT they are also 25% sugar which makes them extremely acidifying when we consume them.

Dr Young has also tested the blood (through live blood analysis) of over 40,000 people and has seen first hand the effect different foods have on the body. So his classification of acid/alkaline foods is really the most accurate and the most relevant to the effect foods have on our pH levels.

4   Where do I get protein from?

One of the first questions people ask when they start the alkaline diet (or any vegetarian life-style) is - what about protein?

The first question here SHOULD BE how much protein do you need? For most people this is not as high as you'd think, and getting enough is actually really easy. The mainstream media would have you believe you would need somewhere between 0.8g and 1.5g (some up to 2g) of protein per 1kg of body weight (2.2lbs).

At the other end of the spectrum, many nutritionists recommend no more than 5g per day, as you build strong bones and muscles with blood NOT protein and you build blood with green foods and green drinks - not protein.

I believe it is somewhere in between.

Most moderately active people would certainly need not more than 30g per day, but on this weight loss journey you are aiming to exercise regularly and build lean muscle mass - so I would aim for between 30-50g per day.

By following the recipes in this book you will NOT have to worry about protein intake - it will all be in there for you in your oats, quinoa, nuts & seeds, dark green leafy vegetables, tofu, nut milks, legumes and chickpeas, lentils and brown rice, sprouts and all of these other wonderful plant-based sources of protein!

Honestly it is really very very easy to hit your protein targets on a plant based diet and animal-based protein is never a good option.

According to T. Collin Campbell, Ph.D., who wrote the book, The China Study,

"Even small intakes of animal foods - meat, eggs, and milk - are associated with significant increases of chronic degenerative diseases."

After forty years of research on the impact of nutrition on human health, T. Collin Campbell concluded: "People who ate the most animal-based foods got the most chronic disease. People who ate the most plant-based foods were the healthiest and tended to avoid chronic disease."

Here is an example day on an alkaline diet and the protein you'd receive:

Alkaline Oats (18g protein)
Avocado on 'Toast' (3g protein)
Power Salad (15g protein)
Vegetables with Red Pepper Dip (3g protein)
Chilli Lime Steam Fry (8g protein, 20g if tofu is used)

On this example menu (with all recipes that are in this book or in your bonus recipes) you'd get 47-61g of protein on that day.

There is not a problem here!

Love Living Energized
Smoothie (p32)

Making it **Easy**

As mentioned earlier in this book, I have been coaching the alkaline diet for over nine years now and I have developed a way of implementing the alkaline diet that makes it very easy for people to follow and stick to. My big three things I have always focused on are to make the alkaline diet EASY, ENJOYABLE and SUSTAINABLE!

I have developed a way of teaching the alkaline lifestyle that is focused entirely around strategies and systems. I truly believe that getting alkaline is all about following a set of strategies and systems that are proven to work and then making those strategies as easy and simple to follow as possible.

So before we get into the recipes, let's take a look at what some of my most powerful, simple strategies are to make the alkaline diet easy, enjoyable and sustainable!

1 Don't Strive for Perfection

In all of my experience of working with tens of thousands of people who want to get alkaline, people from all different countries, backgrounds, with different motivations, goals and with different perspectives - 95% of the people who start of striving for perfection fail within a week, and a lot of them then give up forever.

Let's be straight here - when you change your diet there is more than just food involved. There is your social life, identity, lifestyle, habits, rewards, routines and all sorts of other physical, psychological and social elements at play. Changing everything all at once is just too hard. Unless you are faced with an incredibly powerful and uncompromising reason for motivation, such as a diagnosis of a serious health concern, changing everything all at once and going for perfection is unlikely to succeed.

I am not 100% alkaline now. I never will be. Getting alkaline, being happy, and feeling not only the health and vitality that alkaline living brings but also still enjoying life, having a social life and feeling relaxed and contented is all about balance.

Please do not start this programme thinking you have to be perfect, cut out ALL acidic foods, change your identity, tell your friends you're never going out for coffees or wines ever again and try to never, ever have a single treat ever again in your life. If you do that, it is incredibly likely that you'll fail.

Instead, set realistic goals. Start slowly. Aim to be, for the first few weeks, 50% alkaline (meaning 50% of the foods you eat will be alkaline forming). Pick a few big changes to make and just stick to ONLY those until you have them sorted. For example you might choose to get breakfast sorted, and focus ONLY on breakfast for a few weeks until you have it in the bag. THEN you might move on to lunch. Or you could work on increasing your green foods and hydration (see below) for now and not worry about anything else for a few weeks.

Whatever your strategy, don't make it "To Be Perfect". Go easy on yourself, transition slowly, set realistic targets and aim for a slower, but constant improvement.

It took me a long, long time to get to the place I am now, but I LOVE where I am now. I am 80% alkaline, and I love the energy and vitality this brings - BUT I still have the flexibility and freedom to have a social life, to have the odd blow out and to have treats. But the best part is, I know I can have these blow outs safe in the knowledge that I absolutely know, in my core, that they're not going to spiral out of control. I know that right after I'll be right back on it again.

This is where I want you to get to - but it can only realistically happen if you take your time, transition, go easy on yourself and take it at your own pace.

2 Go Green (Really Green!)

One of the most eye-opening things I've learned from working with so many people over so many years is this: 99% of people eat almost no leafy green foods. Most people get maximum ONE serve per day on average, often less. Sometimes a little more, but more often less.

Let's look at an 'average' mainstream, Joe Public diet for an average day:

Breakfast: Toast, or cereal with milk and a coffee or tea
Mid-Morning Snack: Cup of tea or coffee, maybe some fruit or some biscuits or cookies
Lunch: Sandwich with salad and chicken or beef, or possibly even just a chicken salad
Afternoon Snack: Another tea or something from the bakery
Dinner: Spaghetti bolognaise / risotto / meat & veg / pizza etc.

Can you see what I mean here? There is somewhere between 0.5 - 1 serves of leafy greens in there. This is nowhere near enough. If you want to very quickly have a life full of energy, you need to get at least five serves of leafy greens per day - not just veggies - but leafy greens. This is really easy to do, but if you do it you will feel a HUGE difference.

My biggest tip for this is to serve a side salad with every lunch and dinner you have. In this recipe book you will find lots of delicious salads, but even if you just have one serve of spinach and one serve of lettuce, you'll be at four serves for the day before you've had any juices or other greens as part of your meals!

Doing JUST THIS will make a HUGE impact on your health and energy.

3 Crowd Out the Bad

This is an important change in approach for many people when they first start the alkaline diet and sits well with Strategy #1 above. The concept is simple, when you are trying to get alkaline, focus ONLY on getting the good food in. Sounds simple? Good. It should. It's a really simple approach and has just three Rules of Success to make it happen!

Rule #1 Don't Worry About Cutting Stuff Out

Seriously. Forget cutting anything out. Do what you want. If you still want to have a coffee have one. If you still want to have meat with your dinner have it. If you still want a dessert have it.

The very slight but powerful distinction here is that you're having a conversation with your subconscious mind and your conscious mind to make considered decisions. You're not mindlessly having these foods, you're consciously allowing yourself the possibility of having them - you're not restricting yourself, going cold turkey with anything or telling your brain that stuff is banned.

I know this sounds too good to be true right now, but it's not. So make a mental note - you don't have to stress or worry about cutting the bad stuff out. Just erase it from your thinking for now, relax, enjoy and approach your health free from pressure and anxiety.

Rule #2 Focus on Getting the Good Stuff In

So here is the other side of the bargain. You're allowed to completely forget about eliminating the bad stuff BUT you have to get the good stuff in, in abundance. You have to eat your greens, you have to have salads, you have to have juices and smoothies, you have to have healthy fats and veggies. This is the deal.

The basic (but very effective) premise here is that the good will crowd out the bad, bit by bit. If you commit to having at least 5 serves of green vegetables each day, 3 litres of alkaline water each day, a fresh vegetable juice at least 3 times per week (preferably daily) and so on and build on this every day and every week you'll soon find that you'll get more and more alkaline and eat more and more healthy at your own, natural pace that is right for you.

You'll also feel more satisfied and more energised: unhealthy foods are nutrient poor and leave you feeling hungry very quickly, whereas healthy foods are nutrient dense. When you eat them you feel satisfied for longer because they give your body the nutrients it is craving. So when you focus on getting the good in, it literally will crowd out the bad.

Getting full, satisfied, satiated all day, every day is really easy when you eat good foods. So Rule #2 - Focus on Getting the Good Stuff In - really does work - it's really easy. Each meal you just start with the good stuff first. The plate MUST be clean of the good stuff at the end of the meal.

Rule #3 Follow Your Instincts

This rule is the best bit. This is what I love so much about this approach. The traditional approach to the alkaline diet (and any healthy living plan) requires you to start off by cutting out lots of unhealthy stuff and replacing it with healthy stuff. It immediately puts you on the back foot and makes it a challenge and something you have to battle from day one. When you use this approach of transitioning, you let your subconscious decide when you're ready to progress. Here is how it works: The more alkaline you get the more alkaline you WILL get. It's like the 'rich get richer' analogy. It compounds and snowballs. You can start as slowly as you like with this approach because the best part is - as you focus on getting the good stuff in you will NATURALLY start to remove the bad stuff.

There will be a combination of conscious and subconscious motivation at play:

Conscious: The better you feel the more likely you will be to WANT to make the right choice. After a few days, or a few weeks - or even a few months, you will find yourself WANTING to say no to certain foods or drinks because you're feeling so great and you don't want to change that.

Subconscious: Your subconscious is a fast learner and it works on rewards and the longer you do this the better and better you'll start to feel. Your brain will notice the action equals positive response in your body and it will put two and two together very quickly. The best part of this is - it will then start to act as a 'healthy filter' for you - you'll stop noticing temptations, you'll stop being drawn towards them.

This is why this works so well and why it has worked every single time I've coached someone to implement it.

Dispelling the Myths of the Alkaline Diet

I get emails every day by people who read sites like Quackwatch or hear from misinformed Doctors (who of course, have never actually studied nutrition) and who ask me about the two biggest myths surrounding the alkaline diet:

1) "How can the alkaline diet be true - your stomach is acidic, so it doesn't matter what you eat, it all ends up acid anyway"
2) "Why bother, your body keeps your pH at 7.365 no matter what you do - you can't make your body more alkaline with foods"

Both of these arguments, on face value sound plausible, but they both demonstrate a complete lack of knowledge about nutrition, the body and a complete misunderstanding about the alkaline approach to health.

Let me start by saying, neither of those points are in question:

1) Yes, the stomach can and does produce hydrochloric acid.
2) Yes, the body will always maintain a pH of 7.365 and yes, it's true you can't change this with food.

But both arguments against the alkaline diet miss the mark entirely. Let me explain:

1 Your stomach is acidic, so it doesn't matter what you eat, it all ends up acid anyway.

Yes, the stomach has the capacity to create hydrochloric acid (HCl) and it does this when we digest foods. HOWEVER, the stomach is not a pit full of acid, the HCl that is produced is produced as a by product of digestion. Upon consumption of food, the stomach produces sodium bicarbonate to alkalise the foods we eat as part of the digestive process - the stomach FIRST creates sodium bicarbonate, and then creates the HCl as a by-product of this. The issues occur when there is an OVER-production of HCl - more than the body can alkalise and handle.

There are two situations that can occur:

1) We consume alkaline foods, which do not trigger the release of much sodium bicarbonate (because it's not needed) and then the hydrochloric acid.

2) We consume acidic foods which lead to a big increase in sodium bicarbonate production and an overstimulation and overproduction of HCl which then cannot be eliminated and that's where the issues start.

It really does matter what you eat - the HCl production in the stomach is something we want to minimise at all costs! The more acidic foods and drinks we consume the more sodium bicarbonate is produced, in order to buffer the acids of the acidic foods we've eaten. What this leaves you with is that stomach full of the leftover acid - and this is where all manner of problems start.

When we eat alkaline foods, digestion is easy - the stomach doesn't need to consume sodium bicarbonate to alkalise these foods and so the HCl is not produced and left behind either! This excess of HCl in the pit of the stomach is the root cause of the problems of an acidic lifestyle.

2 Your body stays at pH 7.365 no matter what you eat - you can't make your body more alkaline.

Let's start with the facts. The body has to maintain a pH of 7.365 in the blood and other cells and cellular fluid - and it will do ANYTHING and EVERYTHING it takes to do that. If your pH deviates from that you die, pretty much. Just like with your temperature - your body will regulate at all costs. No matter what it has to do - it will keep your pH at 7.365.

So if you eat a load of acid forming foods, your body will stay at that pH. If you drink a load of super acid drinks like soda, your body will keep that pH. If you do nothing but smoke cigars all day, your body will stay at that pH.

Your body is amazing. It will protect you in the short-term no matter WHAT you do to it! It is this maintaining the pH, the regulating of the pH - the constant battle to stay at the slightly alkaline pH of 7.365 that is caused by our excessively acidic modern lifestyle, that causes the problem.

We fully know and understand that the body will ALWAYS keep this pH of 7.365 and our aim is not to change it! Our aim is to give the body the tools it needs so that maintaining this pH is as easy as possible. Putting lots and lots of acid-forming foods puts the body into a huge tailspin and the damage snowballs. The constant consumption of over-acidic foods and an over-acidic lifestyle leads to massive long term problems. The body will make all manner of long-term sacrifices to your health in order to maintain your short term health by keeping the pH of those cellular fluids at 7.365.

Calcium is pulled from the bones, magnesium is pulled from the muscle, and yeasts, bacteria and microform overgrowths become highly present in the digestive system - clogging your intestines and causing all manner of problems.

The alkaline diet is not aiming to change this 7.365 - it's aiming to support the body, remove the stress of an acidic lifestyle and give the body the tools it needs to thrive.

How To Use This Book

While this is, of course, just a recipe book - it is a very important recipe book that actually does more than just give you some recipes!

Not knowing what to cook is the #1 reason why most people struggle with the alkaline diet

This book provides the fundamental basis on which you can build your alkaline lifestyle. As I explained above, my number one goal for this book was to give you real food - real recipes - that you could actually cook and enjoy.

So as you go through this book and start to incorporate these recipes into your life I recommend you do so with the following three principles in mind:

1 **Go Slow:** I've been helping people to successfully transition to an alkaline lifestyle for many years now and the most obvious difference to me between those who succeed and those who fail is that those who succeed - 99% of the time - go slow and take it easy. They transition. When people go cold turkey (no pun intended) they usually only last a few days, if that.

2 **Find Your Faves:** Something that really helped me to make this lifestyle permanent was working the meals that a) I enjoyed the most; b) found quickest and easiest to cook; and c) frequently had the right ingredients for. Go through the book and pick four or five of these and make sure you've always got the core ingredients of that meal in the pantry.

3 **Plan Ahead:** Being underprepared is the next biggest reason why people fail to reach their health goals. When the fridge is empty - we snack. And when the fridge is empty, the snacks are always unhealthy. The same goes for takeaway - it is almost always ordered when we don't have anything in to cook! So go through this recipe book, pick out your meals for the week and then shop for them a few days in advance!

A Few Notes...

Translations!

Energise is UK-based and therefore we're always writing in UK-English. Sorry about that. As a few of you reading this might be based elsewhere I thought it might be handy to include a few conversions and translations. Note: where Himalayan salt is used, you can use any 'healthy' salt i.e. please don't use normal table salt!

UK	Non-UK
Aubergine	Eggplant
Courgette	Zucchini
Coriander	Cilantro
Beetroot	Beets
Broad Beans	Fava Beans
Chard	Silver Beet
Chickpeas	Garbanzo Beans
Haricot Beans	Navy Beans
Mangetout	Snowpeas
Pepper	Capsicum or Sweet Pepper
Rocket	Arugula
Spring Onions	Scallions
Stock	Broth
Stock Cube	Bouillon Cubes

Cooking Conversions

1 militers = 1/5 teaspoon
5 ml = 1 teaspoon
15 ml = 1 tablespoon
34 ml = 1 fluid oz.
100 ml = 3.4 fluid oz.
240 ml = 1 cup
1 liter = 34 fluid oz.
1 liter = 4.2 cups
1 liter = 2.1 pints
1 liter = 1.06 quarts
1 liter = .26 gallon

1 gram = .035 ounce
100 grams = 3.5 ounces
500 grams = 1.10 pounds
1 kilogram = 2.205 pounds
1 kilogram = 35 oz.

Health Benefits

All the recipes featured in this book are packed with vitamins and minerals to help you reach certain goals. We've carefully studied the nutritional content in each recipe to see which of the recipes are best suited to each specific aim.

Heart Health

Alka-Tropical Smoothie
Alkaline French Dressing
Alkaline Gazpacho
Alkaline Lentil Ratatouille
Alkaline Pistou Soup
Anti-Oxidant Super Meal
Broccoli and Potato Curry
Broccoli with Tahini
Broccoli, Carrots and Peas in Coconut Curry Sauce
Chickpea and Avocado Mash
Chickpea Kale Rolls with Tomato Salsa
Chickpea Korma with Brown Rice
Chickpea Patties with Tomato, Cucumber & Mint Salad
Chilli Tofu Pita Breads
Chinese Stir Fry Buckwheat Noodles
Corn Salsa Salad
Courgette Rolls with Pesto and Red Pepper Dip
Digestion Juice
Energising Muesli Mix
Fennel Soup
Garlic Tofu with Vietnamese Coleslaw with Lime Dressing
Ginger Green Refresher
Gluten-Free Spinach Garlic Tofu Burgers
Green Veggie Smoothie
Leafy Greens & Ginger Stir Fry
Lettuce Tacos
Lime Green Smoothie
Metabolic Fire Smoothie
Metabolism Booster Juice
Metabolism Ignition Juice
Mexican Tortilla Soup
Mixed Avocado Salad
Nut Chips
Pepper-y Fire Green Juice
Radicchio, Artichoke and Walnut Salad
Red Lentils with Peppers
Ribollita Vegetable Bean Soup
Rocket, Watercress and Mint Salad
Salmon Steak with Broccoli
Salsa Fresca
Soba Noodle, Seaweed & Thai Vegetable Salad
Spicy Aubergine Pasta
Tofu Brazil Nut Steam Fry
Vegetable Dhal with Ginger Raita
Warm Quinoa Savory Breakfast

Weight Loss

Alka-Tropical Smoothie
Alkaline Quinoa Salad with Avocado
Alkaline Root Vegetable Curry
Alkaline Courgette Soup
Anti-Oxidant Super Meal
Aubergine Stew with Spicy Chickpeas
Avocado Summer Mexican Salad
Baby Pea & Broad Bean Spread
Beetroot Lemonade
Big Bad Green Drink
Black Bean Hummous
Broccoli Blend
Broccoli Cream Soup
Chickpea Korma with Brown Rice
Coconut Quinoa and Sweet Potato Curry
Courgette Delight
Courgette Rolls with Pesto and Red Pepper Dip
Energise Green Smoothie MK II
Gluten-Free Spinach Garlic Tofu Burgers
Grilled Aubergine with Salsa Fresca
Leafy Greens and Ginger Stir Fry
Metabolism Ignition Juice
Nut Chips
Soba Pasta Pesto Pine Extravaganza!
Spiced Turnips with Spinach and Tomatoes
Super Hearty Minestrone
Sweet Potato Soup
Warm Broccoli Salad

Bad Breath

Alka-Tropical Smoothie
Alkaline Root Vegetable Curry
Alkaline Courgette Soup
Avocado Summer Mexican Salad
Baby Pea & Broad Bean Spread
Greens & Grapefruit Smoothie
Beetroot Lemonade
Big Bad Green Drink
Broccoli Cream Soup
Coconut Quinoa and Sweet Potato Curry
Coriander, Mint and Chilli Dressing
Grilled Aubergine with Salsa Fresca
Spiced Turnips with Spinach and Tomatoes
Warm Broccoli Salad

Liver Health

Alkaline Asian Dressing
Alkaline Quinoa Salad with Avocado
Alkalising Chilli Spring Greens
Aubergine Stew with Spicy Chickpeas
Black Bean Hummous
Broccoli and Potato Curry
Broccoli Blend
Carrot and Artichoke Soup
Chinese Stir Fry Buckwheat Noodles
Courgette and Split Pea Soup
Courgette Delight
Eastern Pesto!
Energise Green Smoothie MK II
Energising Muesli Mix
Fennel with Brown Basmati Rice
Garlic 'Mayonnaise'
Lime Green Smoothie
Red Pepper, Walnut and Almond Omega Spread
Salmon Steak with Broccoli
Smooth Avocado and Tofu Dip
Soba Pasta Pesto Pine Extravaganza!
Super Hearty Minestrone
Sweet Potato Soup
Spinach with Almonds

Osteoporosis

Alkaline French Dressing
Alkaline Sushi Rolls
Alkalising Chilli Spring Greens
Avocado on Toast
Greens & Grapefruit Smoothie
Broccoli and Potato Curry
Carrot & Artichoke Soup
Carrot Dip
Chinese Stir Fry Buckwheat Noodles
Courgettes with Moroccan Spices
Eastern Pesto!
Fennel with Brown Basmati Rice
Lime Green Smoothie
Mixed Sprouts Salad
Oat & Almonds Pancakes
Red Pepper, Walnut and Almond Omega Spread
Salmon Steak with Broccoli
Smooth Avocado & Tofu Dip
Soaked Almonds
Tomato & Basil Sauce

Digestion

Alkaline French Dressing
Alkaline Gazpacho
Alkaline Lentil Ratatouille
Alkaline Pistou Soup
Alkaline Tomato and Asparagus Soup
Alkalising Chilli Spring Greens
Baby Pea & Broad Bean Spread
Big Bad Green Drink
Broccoli Cream Soup
Broccoli with Tahini
Broccoli, Carrots and Peas in Coconut Curry Sauce
Carrot Dip
Chickpea and Avocado Mash
Chickpea Kale Rolls with Tomato Salsa
Chickpea Patties with Tomato, Cucumber & Mint Salad
Chilli Tofu Pita Breads
Cool Quinoa Summer Salad
Coriander, Mint and Chilli Dressing
Courgette and Split Pea Soup
Eastern Pesto!
Fennel Soup
Ginger Green Refresher
Green Veggie Smoothie
Grilled Aubergine with Salsa Fresca
Almost Alkaline Pizza
Kale Chickpea Mash
Kohlrabi Salad with Vegetable Dressing
Lamb's Lettuce with Walnuts & Avocado
Leek and Asparagus Soup
Lettuce Tacos
Marinated Salmon Fillet Asian Style
Metabolic Fire Smoothie
Metabolic Booster Juice
Mexican Tortilla Soup
Mixed Avoado Salad
Mixed Sprouts Salad
Moroccan Vegetable Soup
Oriental Vegetable Stew with Chickpeas
Pearl Barley Salad
Peppery Fire Green Juice
Radicchio, Artichoke and Walnut Salad
Red Lentils with Peppers
Ribollita Vegetable Bean Soup
Roasted Artichokes with Lemon Oil Dip
Romanesco Cauliflower Curry
Salsa Fresca
Smooth Avocado & Tofu Dip
Soba Noodle, Seaweed & Thai Vegetable Salad
Spelt Pasta with Broccoli and Almonds
Spiced Turnips with Spinach and Tomatoes
Spicy Aubergine Pasta
Tahini and Lemon Dressing
Tofu Brazil Nut Steam Fry
Tunisian Chickpea Soup
Vegetable Dahl with Ginger Raita
Vegetable Sticks
Warm Red Pepper, Spinach and Courgette Salad
Warm Winter CerealSpinach and Chickpeas

Libido

Alkaline Sushi Rolls
Avocado on Toast
Coconut Scented Rice with Toasted Almonds & Mint
Courgettes with Moroccan Spices
Garlic Tofu with Vietnamese Coleslaw and Lime Dressing
Oat & Almond Pancakes
Tomato and Basil Sauce

Candida

Alkaline French Dressing
Alkaline Open Sandwich
Alkaline Tomato & Asparagus Soup
Autumn Pumpkin Stew
Carrot Dip
Coconut Scented Rice with Toasted Almonds & Mint
Cool Quinoa Summer Salad
Coriander, Mint and Chlili Dressing
Corn Salsa Salad
Digestion Juice
Eastern Pesto
Fennel Soup
Almost Alkaline Pizza
Kale Chickpea Mash
Lamb's Lettuce with Walnuts & Avocado
Leek and Asparagus Soup
Lemon & Ginger Drink
Marinated Salmon Fillet Asian Style
Metabolism Booster Juice
Mixed Avocado Salad
Mixed Sprouts Salad
Moroccan Vegetable Soup
Okra with Coriander and Tomatoes
Oriental Vegetable Stew with Chickpeas
Pearl Barley Salad
Raddichio, Artichoke and Walnut Salad
Raw Avocado and Tomato Soup
Roasted Artichokes with Lemon Oil Dip
Rocket, Watercress and Mint Salad
Romanesco Cauliflower Curry
Smooth Avocado & Tofu Dip
Soba Noodle, Seaweed & Thai Vegetable Salad
Spelt Pasta with Broccoli and Almonds
Tahini and Lemon Dressing
Tofu Brazil Nut Steam Fry
Tunisian Chickpea Soup
Vegetable Sticks
Warm Red Pepper, Spinach and Courgette Salad
Warm Winter Cereal
'Creamy' Brussels Sprouts

Cholesterol

Alkaline French Dressing
Alkaline Sushi Rolls
Alkaline Courgette Soup
Avocado Summer Mexican Salad
Greens & Grapefruit Smoothie
Beetroot Lemonade
Broccoli and Potato Curry
Broccoli, Carrots and Peas in Coconut Curry Sauce
Carrot Dip
Chickpea Salad with Avocado & Lemon Dressing
Chickpea Kale Rolls with Tomato Salsa
Chinese Stir Fry Buckwheat Noodles
Cleansing Weight Loss Delight
Coconut Quinoa and Sweet Potato Curry
Green Veggie Smoothie
Lime Green Smoothie
Mexican Tortilla Soup
Mixed Sprouts Salad
Oat & Almond Pancake
Pesto Greens & Scrambled Tofu
Salmon Steak with Broccoli
Soaked Almonds
Vegetable Dhal with Ginger Raita
'Creamy' Brussel Sprouts

Acne

Alkaline French Dressing
Alkaline Gazpacho
Alkaline Lentil Ratatouille
Alkaline Open Sandwich
Alkaline Pistou Soup
Alkaline Tomato & Asparagus Soup
Antioxidant Super Meal
Baby Pea & Broad Bean Spread
Big Bad Green Drink
Broccoli Cream Soup
Broccoli with Tahini
Carrot Dip
Chickpea and Avocado Mash
Chickpea Patties with Tomato, Cucumber & Mint Salad
Chilli Tofu Pita Breads
Cool Quinoa Summer Salad
Coriander, Mint and Chilli Dressing
Corn Salsa Salad
Eastern Pesto!
Fennel Soup
Ginger Green Refresher
Gluten-Free Spinach Garlic Tofu Burgers
Grilled Aubergine with Salsa Fresca
Kale Chickpea Mash
Leek and Asparagus Soup
Lettuce Tacos
Metabolic Fire Smoothie
Metabolism Booster Juice
Mixed Avocado Salad
Mixed Sprouts Salad
Moroccan Vegetable Soup
Peppery Fire Green Juice
Red Lentils with Peppers
Red Pepper, Walnut and Almond Omega Spread
Ribollita Vegetable Bean Soup
Roasted Artichokes with Lemon Oil Dip
Romanesco Cauliflower Curry
Salsa Fresca
Smooth Avocado & Tofu Dip
Soba Noodle, Seaweed & Thai Vegetable Salad
Spiced Turnips with Spinach and Tomatoes
Spicy Aubergine Pasta
Tofu Brazil Nut Steam Fry
Vegetable Sticks
Warm Quinoa Savory Breakfast
Warm Red Pepper, Spinach and Courgette Salad
Spinach and Chickpeas

Colds & Flu

Alkaline Open Sandwich
Alkaline Tomato & Asparagus Soup
Autumn Pumpkin Stew
Avocado on Toast
Chickpea Salad with Avocado and Lemon Dressing
Cleansing Weight Loss Delight
Cool Quinoa Summer Salad
Coriander, Mint and Chilli Dressing
Courgettes with Moroccan Spices
Digestion Juice
Garlic Tofu with Vietnamese Coleslaw & Lime Dressing
Kale Chickpea Mash
Kohlrabi Salad with Vegetable Dressing
Lemon & Ginger Green Drink
Moroccan Vegetable Soup
Okra with Coriander and Tomatoes
Pesto Greens & Scrambled Tofu
Raw Avocado & Tomate Soup
Rocket, Watercress & Mint Salad
Romanesco Cauliflower Curry
Tomato & Baisl Sauce
Vegetable Sticks

Kidney

- Alkaline Quinoa Salad with Avocado
- Alkaline Root Vegetable Curry
- Alkalising Chilli Spring Greens
- Almond Metabolism Smoothie
- Aubergine Stew with Spicy Chickpeas
- Black Bean Hummous
- Broccoli Blend
- Carrot and Artichoke Soup
- Courgette Delight
- Energise Green Smoothie MK II
- Fennel with Brown Basmati Rice
- Red Pepper, Walnut, and Almond Omega Spread
- Soba Pasta Pesto Pine Extravaganza!
- Super Hearty Minestrone
- Sweet Potato Soup
- Warm Broccoli Salad
- Spinach with Almonds

Bloating

- Alka-Tropical Smoothie
- Alkaline Quinoa Salad with Avocado
- Alkaline Root Vegetable Curry
- Almond Metabolism Smoothie
- Antioxidant Super Meal
- Aubergine Stew with Spicy Chickpeas
- Black Bean Hummous
- Broccoli Blend
- Broccoli with Tahini
- Chickpea Korma with Brown Rice
- Courgette Delight
- Courgette Rolls with Pesto and Red Pepper Dip
- Energise Green Smoothie MK II
- Energising Muesli Mix
- Ginger Green Refresher
- Gluten-Free Spinach Garlic Tofu Burgers
- Leafy Greens & Ginger Stir Fry
- Metabolism Ignition Juice
- Nut Chips
- Soba Pasta Pesto Pine Extravaganza!
- Super Hearty Minestrone
- Sweet Potato Soup
- Warm Broccoli Salad
- Warm Quinoa Savory Breakfast
- Spinach with Almonds

Chronic Fatigue

- Almond Metabolism Smoothie
- Baby Pea & Broad Bean Spread
- Big Bad Green Drink
- Broccoli Cream Soup
- Digestion Juice
- Grilled Aubergine with Salsa Fresca
- Rocket, Watercress and Mint Salad
- Soaked Almonds
- Spiced Turnips with Spinach and Tomatoes
- Spinach and Chickpeas

Blood Pressure

- Alkaline Sushi Rolls
- Alkaline Courgette Soup
- Avocado on Toast
- Avocado Summer Mexican Salad
- Greens & Grapefruit Smoothie
- Beetroot Lemonade
- Broccoli and Potato Curry
- Broccoli, Carrots & Peas in Coconut Curry Sauce
- Chickpea Salad with Avocado & Lemon Dressing
- Chickpea Kale Rolls with Tomato Salsa
- Chinese Stir Fry Buckwheat Noodles
- Cleansing Weight Loss Delight
- Coconut Quinoa and Sweet Potato Curry
- Courgette and Split Pea Soup
- Courgettes with Moroccan Spices
- Green Veggie Smoothie
- Almost Alkaline Pizza
- Kohlrabi Salad with Vegetable Dressing
- Lamb's Lettuce with Walnuts & Avocado
- Lemon & Ginger Green Drink
- Lime Green Smoothie
- Marinated Salmon Fillet Asian Style
- Mexican Tortilla Soup
- Oat & Almond Pancakes
- Oriental Vegetable Stew with Chickpeas
- Pearl Barley Salad
- Pesto Greens & Scrambled Tofu
- Salmon Steak with Broccoli
- Spelt Pasta with Broccoli and Almonds
- Tahini and Lemon Dressing
- Tomato & Basil Sauce
- Tunisian Chickpea Soup
- Vegetable Dahl with Ginger Raita
- Warm Winter Cereal
- 'Creamy Brussel Sprouts'

Eczema

- Alkaline Open Sandwich
- Alkaline Courgette Soup
- Autumn Pumpkin Stew
- Avocado Summer Mexican Salad
- Beetroot Lemonade
- Broccoli, Carrots & Peas in Coconut Curry Sauce
- Chickpea Salad with Avocado & Lemon Dressing
- Chickpea Kale Rolls with Tomato Salsa
- Cleansing Weight Loss Delight
- Coconut Quinoa and Sweet Potato Curry
- Digestion Juice
- Green Veggie Smoothie
- Kale Chickpea Mash
- Kohlrabi Salad with Vegetable Dressing
- Leek and Asparagus Soup
- Lemon & Ginger Green Drink
- Mexican Tortilla Soup
- Moroccan Vegetable Soup
- Okra with Coriander and Tomatoes
- Pesto Greens and Scrambled Tofu
- Raw Avocado and Tomato Soup
- Roasted Artichokes with Lemon Oil Dip
- Rocket, Watercress and Mint Salad
- Salsa Fresca
- Tahini and Lemon Dressing
- Vegetable Dhal with Ginger Raita
- Vegetable Sticks
- 'Creamy' Brussel Sprouts

Energy

- Alkaline Quinoa Salad with Avocado
- Almond Metabolism Smoothie
- Aubergine Stew with Spicy Chickpeas
- Black Bean Hummous
- Broccoli Blend
- Carrot and Artichoke Soup
- Chickpea Korma with Brown Rice
- Courgette Delight
- Courgette Rolls with Pesto and Pepper Dip
- Energise Green Smoothie MK II
- Energising Muesli Mix
- Fennel with Brown Basmati Rice
- Leafy Greens and Ginger Stir-Fry
- Metabolism Ignition Juice
- Nut Chips
- Soba Pasta Pesto Pine Extravaganza!
- Sweet Potato Soup
- Spinach with Almonds

Digestion

- Autumn Pumpkin Stew
- Coconut Scented Rice with Toasted Almonds & Mint
- Corn Salsa Salad
- Almost Alkaline Pizza
- Lamb's Lettuce with Walnuts and Avocado
- Lemon & Ginger Green Drink
- Marinated Salmon Fillet Asian Style
- Metabolism Booster Juice
- Mixed Avocado Salad
- Okra with Coriander and Tomatoes
- Oriental Vegetable Stew with Chickpeas
- Pearl Barley Salad
- Radicchio, Artichoke and Walnut Salad
- Raw Avocado and Tomato Soup
- Soba Noodle, Seaweed & Thai Vegetable Salad
- Spelt Pasta with Broccoli and Almonds
- Tofu Brazil Nut Steam Fry
- Tunisian Chickpea Soup
- Warm Winter Cereal

Constipation

- Autumn Pumpkin Stew
- Chickpea Salad with Avocado and Lemon Dressing
- Cleansing Weight Loss Delight
- Coconut Scented Rice with Toasted Almonds & Mint
- Courgettes with Moroccan Spices
- Garlic Tofu with Vietnamese Coleslaw
- Lamb's Lettuce with Walnuts and Avocado
- Lemon & Ginger Green Drink
- Marinated Salmon Fillet Asian Style
- Okra with Coriander and Tomatoes
- Oriental Vegetable Stew with Chickpeas
- Raw Avocado and Tomato Soup
- Spelt Pasta with Broccoli and Almonds
- Tunisian Chickpea Soup
- Warm Winter Cereal

Juices & Smoothies

Metabolism Booster Juice

Burn more fats with this highly refreshing juice!

Serves: 2
Preparation Time: 30 Minutes

Ingredients:
2 large handfuls of spinach
1 large grapefruit
1 medium carrot
2 celery stalks
1/4 beet
Sprinkle of cinnamon (added and stirred in after)
1/2 inch of fresh stem ginger

Instructions:

1 Thoroughly wash all of the ingredients and chop to size to fit your juicer. Juice in a random order, rather than all of one ingredient and then all of the next. Once all of the ingredients are gone, wash a little water through the juicer (if your juicer allows this). Consume as soon as possible.

Nutritional Highlights:

This recipe is beneficial for:

Heart Health
Acne
Digestion
IBS
Candida

Each serve contains the following RDA %'s:

Protein	10%
Vitamin A	322%
Vitamin C	114%
Vitamin E	10%
Vitamin K	624%
Riboflavin	11%
Vitamin B6	12%
Folate	57%
Calcium	10%
Iron	15%
Magnesium	20%
Potassium	24%
Manganese	58%
Dietary Fibre	11%

Big Bad Green Drink

Jumpstart Your Mornings with Ross's Ultimate Green Drink Recipe

Serves: 2
Preparation Time: 10 Minutes

Ingredients:
One stalk of kale (or a handful if you buy it off the stalk)
4 sticks of chard
2 handfuls of baby spinach leaves
2 sticks of celery
1 (1/2 if its a biggie) cucumber
5 broccoli florets
1 inch of raw root ginger

Instructions:

1 Juice it all through your juicer, putting the ginger in with something that is high-water such as the cucumber. Enjoy immediately and feel the buzz!

Nutritional Highlights:

This recipe is beneficial for:

Acne
Digestion
Chronic Fatigue
Bad breath
Weight Loss

Each serve contains the following RDA %'s:

Protein	21%
Vitamin A	590%
Vitamin C	254%
Vitamin E	28%
Vitamin K	3237%
Riboflavin	28%
Vitamin B6	30%
Calcium	20%
Iron	35%
Magnesium	65%
Potassium	45%
Sodium	41%
Manganese	81%
Folate	59%
Dietary Fibre	28%

Metabolism Ignition Juice

Juice Your Way to a Slimmer and Healthier Body with this Winner!

Serves: 2
Preparation Time: 5 Minutes

Ingredients:
1 cucumber
1 lemon
Handful kale
Handful spinach
Handful flat leaf parsley
2 stalks celery
1/4 bulb fennel
1/3 head lettuce
1 inch piece ginger

Instructions:

1. Thoroughly wash all of the ingredients and chop to size to fit your juicer. Juice in a random order, rather than all of one ingredient and then all of the next. Once all of the ingredients are gone, wash a little water through the juicer (if your juicer allows this). Consume as soon as possible.

Nutritional Highlights:

This recipe is beneficial for:

Heart Health
Immune System
Energy
Weight Loss
Bloating

Each serve contains the following RDA %'s:

Protein	33%
Vitamin K	711%
Vitamin C	539%
Vitamin A	2508%
Riboflavin	34%
Vitamin B6	46%
Folate	22%
Potassium	22%
Manganese	44%
Magnesium	30%
Copper	63%
Calcium	34%
Zinc	92%
Dietary Fibre	57%

Digestion Juice

Promote a healthy digestive system with this amazing juice!

Serves: 2
Preparation Time: 5 Minutes

Ingredients:
1/3 head of white cabbage, leaves
separated and cleaned
2 handfuls of spinach
1 cucumber
1/2 inch of ginger
1/2 lemon
1 small bunch of fresh mint

Instructions:

1 Thoroughly wash all of the ingredients and chop to size to fit your
juicer. Juice in a random order, rather than all of one ingredient
and then all of the next. Once all of the ingredients are gone,
wash a little water through the juicer (if your juicer allows this).
Consume as soon as possible.

Nutritional Highlights:

This recipe is beneficial for:

Heart Health
Candida
Eczema
Colds & Flu
Chronic Fatigue

Each serve contains the
following RDA %'s:

Protein	15%
Vitamin A	218%
Vitamin C	209%
Vitamin K	666%
Vitamin B6	12%
Calcium	19%
Iron	28%
Magnesium	36%
Phosphorus	12%
Potassium	34%
Copper	31%
Manganese	73%
Folate	13%
Dietary Fibre	89%

Lemon & Ginger Green Drink

A more fruity flavoured green drink to help mix it up!

Serves: 2
Preparation Time: 10 Minutes

Ingredients:
2 lemons, peeled
1/2 red grapefruit, peeled
2 celery stalks
2 large carrots
1 cucumber
1 1/2 inch of fresh root ginger
Handful of parsley
Handful of mint
Pinch of stevia to taste

Instructions:

1 Peel the fruits and juice everything.

2 Add stevia if necessary, to taste.

Nutritional Highlights:

This recipe is beneficial for:

IBS
Candida
Eczema
Colds & Flu
Constipation
Blood Pressure

Each serve contains the following RDA %'s:

Protein	11%
Vitamin K	343%
Vitamin C	161%
Pantothenic Acid	35%
Vitamin A	261%
Vitamin B6	12%
Folate	18%
Potassium	24%
Manganese	24%
Magnesium	14%
Copper	22%
Iron	12%
Calcium	12%
Dietary Fibre	45%

Ginger Green Refresher

A great green drink when you want something to quench the thirst

Serves: 2
Preparation Time: 10 Minutes

Ingredients:
2 cucumbers
Handful of parsley
Handful of mint
Handful of spinach
8 kale leaves
Handful of lettuce leaves
1 inch of fresh root ginger
1 lemon

Instructions:

1   Wash everything and peel the lemon.

2   Juice all of the ingredients, making sure to put the ginger in near
    the start so the other veggies can wash it all through.

Nutritional Highlights:

This recipe is beneficial for:

Heart Health
Immune System
Acne
Digestion
Loss
Bloating

Each serve contains the
following RDA %'s:

Protein	41%
Vitamin A	1368%
Vitamin C	950%
Vitamin K	4735%
Thiamin	36%
Riboflavin	44%
Vitamin B6	68%
Folate	67%
Iron	22%
Magnesium	29%
Potassium	30%
Copper	24%
Manganese	48%
Niacin	20%
Dietary Fibre	65%

Beetroot Lemonade
Who'd have thought beetroot was so yummy!

Serves: 2
Preparation Time: 5 Minutes

Ingredients:
4 medium beetroots
1 lemon peeled
2 inch piece of fresh root ginger
Optional: stevia to taste

Instructions:

1 Simply wash, peel and juice the ingredients and serve over ice on a hot summer's day!

Nutritional Highlights:

This recipe is beneficial for:

Eczema
Anti-Aging
Blood Pressure
Cholesterol
Anti-Inflammatory
Weight Loss

Each serve contains the following RDA %'s:

Protein	4%
Vitamin C	74%
Vitamin B6	7%
Magnesium	6%
Potassium	6%
Copper	13%
Manganese	6%
Calcium	4%
Dietary Fibre	14%

Alka-Tropical Smoothie
A different kind of taste to other alkaline smoothies!

Serves: 2
Preparation Time: 10 Minutes

Ingredients:
1 avocado
1/2 cucumber
1 inch of fresh root ginger, crushed
1 red grapefruit, peeled
2 handfuls of spinach
300ml of coconut water
Ice if desired

Instructions:

1 Peel the grapefruit and roughly chop the cucumber.

2 Blend all ingredients together until smooth.

Nutritional Highlights:

This recipe is beneficial for:

Heart Health
Immune Boosting
Cholesterol
Weight Loss
Bloating
Anti-Aging

Each serve contains the following RDA %'s:

Vitamin K	662%
Vitamin C	112%
Pantothenic Acid	18%
Vitamin A	208%
Riboflavin	18%
Vitamin B6	32%
Folate	74%
Potassium	54%
Manganese	72%
Magnesium	46%
Copper	27%
Iron	23%
Vitamin E	21%
Dietary Fibre	53%

Lime Green Smoothie

A fresh, zingy alkaline smoothie to start the day with a pop!

Serves: 2
Preparation Time: 5 Minutes

Ingredients:
1 avocado
1 cucumber
4 limes (peeled)
2 big handfuls of spinach
Handful of ice cubes
200ml of coconut water or
200ml of alkaline water plus a
pinch of stevia

Instructions:

1. Simply blend all ingredients together in a blender to make a thick, smooth smoothie!

Nutritional Highlights:

This recipe is beneficial for:

Anti-Aging
Immune System
Blood Pressure
Cholesterol
Osteoporosis
Liver Health

Each serve contains the following RDA %'s:

Protein	16%
Vitamin K	662%
Vitamin C	140%
Pantothenic Acid	18%
Vitamin A	194%
Riboflavin	18%
Vitamin B6	28%
Folate	72%
Potassium	45%
Manganese	67%
Magnesium	40%
Copper	21%
Iron	23%
Vitamin E	21%
Dietary Fibre	61%

Love Living Energized Green Smoothie

Get PUMPED with energy and nourish your body in one quick and easy smoothie

Serves: 2
Preparation Time: 5 Minutes

Ingredients:
1/2 cucumber
4 kale leaves
Handful of spinach
Handful of mint
Handful of parsley
1 inch piece of fresh root ginger
1 avocado
1/2 green pepper
1 spring onion
1 lime, juiced
150ml of cooled vegetable stock
Optional: 1 cup coconut water

Instructions:

1 Start by chopping everything roughly (except the leaves) and then start by blending together the avocado and stock or coconut water to make a paste.

2 Then begin adding the other ingredients, tear the kale leaves before adding, throw in the spinach, mint, parsley, pepper, onion.

3 Hand juice in the lime and grate or crush (using a garlic press) in the ginger.

4 Serve and enjoy, with ice if you prefer!

Nutritional Highlights:

This recipe is beneficial for:

Kidney Health
Liver Health
Energy
Weight Loss
Digestive Health
Cholesterol Lowering

Each serve contains the following RDA %'s:

Protein	42%
Vitamin K	4371%
Vitamin C	904%
Pantothenic Acid	20%
Vitamin A	1230%
Riboflavin	41%
Vitamin B6	82%
Folate	91%
Thiamin	38%
Potassium	45%
Manganese	56%
Magnesium	36%
Copper	25%
Iron	28%
Dietary Fibre	90%

Peppery Firey Green Juice

A firey zinger of a green drink!

Serves: 2
Preparation Time: 10 Minutes

Ingredients:
1 cucumber
1 largepiece of fennel
1 stalk celery
Handful of rocket leaves
Handful of spinach
1 lime
1 inch of fresh ginger

Instructions:

1 Peel the lime and juice all ingredients

2 Drink right away! Water it down a little if needed.

Nutritional Highlights:

This recipe is beneficial for:

Gastrointestinal Relief
Anti-Inflammatory
Immune System
Acne
Digestion
PMS

Each serve contains the following RDA %'s:

Protein	14%
Vitamin K	409%
Vitamin C	87%
Vitamin A	131%
Riboflavin	13%
Vitamin B6	15%
Folate	49%
Potassium	40%
Manganese	53%
Magnesium	32%
Phosphorous	15%
Copper	16%
Iron	19%
Calcium	21%
Dietary Fiber	35%

Almond Metabolism Smoothie

Not just healthy - incredibly tasty too!

Serves: 2
Preparation Time: 15 Minutes

Ingredients:
Make 350ml of Almond Milk
(see Almond Milk Recipe)
Handful of organic oats
Handful of chia seeds
Handful of quinoa flakes
Optional: coconut water or milk to taste

Instructions:

1 Prepare the almond milk using a slow gear juicer (such as the Hurom or Oscar) OR using a blender

2 Next add this to a blender and blend in the oats, chia and quinoa flakes and coconut water to taste. If you don't have coconut water, you can use coconut milk.

Nutritional Highlights:

This recipe is beneficial for:

Chronic Fatigue
PMS
Kidney Health
Muscle Development
Bloating
Weight Loss

Each serve contains the following RDA %'s:

Protein	65%
Thiamin	84%
Riboflavin	21%
Vitamin B6	13%
Folate	22%
Pantothenic Acid	21%
Calcium	32%
Iron	45%
Magnesium	84%
Potassium	36%
Zinc	48%
Copper	54%
Manganese	430%
Phosphorus	32%

Metabolic Fire Smoothie

Amp up your Metabolism with this Green Smoothie!

Serves: 2
Preparation Time: 10 Minutes

Ingredients:
1 avocado
2 large handfuls of spinach
1/2 large grapefruit
1 inch of fresh stem ginger, grated
1 cucumber
Handful of parsley
1/2 red pepper
150ml vegetable stock (or dilute to taste)

Instructions:

1   Blend the avocado with 1/2 of the stock to form a paste, and then blend in the cucumber and grapefruit. Once this is smooth add in the remaining ingredients and smooth until blend.

2   Dilute with stock until it's as smooth as you like.

Nutritional Highlights:

This recipe is beneficial for:

Bad Breath
Immune System
Acne
Digestion
PMS
Weight Loss

Each serve contains the following RDA %'s:

Protein	19%
Vitamin A	501%
Vitamin C	394%
Vitamin E	46%
Vitamin K	1901%
Thiamin	30%
Riboflavin	31%
Vitamin B6	61%
Folate	166%
Pantothenic Acid	38%
Iron	51%
Magnesium	67%
Potassium	86%
Manganese	120%
Dietary Fibre	97%

Greens & Grapefruit Smoothie
A different taste to the regular green smoothies - very refreshing!

Serves: 2
Preparation Time: 5 Minutes

Ingredients:
2 grapefruits, peeled and de-seeded
1 avocado
2 cups fresh baby spinach (or other leafy green)
4 ounces of water
1 pinch of stevia

Instructions:

1 Blend everything together then serve! Optional: blend in or add a couple of ice-cubes. This is a really refreshing, very alkaline drink so can work well with ice on a summer's day!

Nutritional Highlights:

This recipe is beneficial for:

Blood Pressure
Cholesterol
Osteoporosis
Bad Breath
PMS
Anti-Aging

Each serve contains the following RDA %'s:

Vitamin K	27%
Folate	25%
Vitamin C	81%
Pantothenic Acid	14%
Vitamin B6	13%
Vitamin E	11%
Vitamin A	31%
Potassium	19%
Copper	10%
Dietary Fibre	32%

Green Veggie Smoothie

A simple, delicious, savoury smoothie

Serves: 2
Preparation Time: 5 Minutes

Ingredients:
1 avocado
1 carrot, medium
2 celery stalks, plus the bits that
are all leafy
2 handfuls baby spinach
2 tomatoes
1 clove garlic, derooted
2.5-3c water

Instructions:

1 Blend everything together then serve!

Nutritional Highlights:

This recipe is beneficial for:

Heart Health
Digestion
Eczema
Blood Pressure
Cholesterol
Anti-Inflammatory

Each serve contains the
following RDA %'s:

Vitamin A	159%
Vitamin C	46%
Vitamin E	10%
Vitamin K	331%
Vitamin B6	15%
Folate	39%
Magnesium	14%
Potassium	21%
Manganese	18%

Other Alkaline Breakfasts

Warm Winter Cereal

Winter warmers for those colder months and fantastic for the digestive system

Serves: 2
Preparation Time: 5 Minutes

Ingredients:
Your choice of any or a mix of:
90g Buckwheat groats, cracked
buckwheat, quinoa, barley
450ml Almond, soy or rice milk
Pinch of cinnamon

Instructions:

1   Mix the grains, nuts and seeds together in two bowls and pour
    in the milk of your choice. I recommend almond milk or hemp
    milk most strongly, but soy or rice milk are fine too. Finish with
    a pinch of cinnamon.

2   If you are transitioning, for the first few weeks you can add a
    few berries.

Nutritional Highlights:

This recipe is beneficial for:

Digestion
IBS
Candida
Constipation
Blood Pressure

Each serve contains the
following RDA %'s:

Protein	26%
Calcium	37%
Vitamin B6	6%
Folate	10%
Iron	8%
Magnesium	15%
Phosphorus	14%
Manganese	40%
Fibre	20%
Potassium	14%
Vitamin A	13%
Vitamin B2	25%
Vitamin B12	50%

Energising Muesli Mix
A great transitional alkaline muesli

Serves: 2
Preparation Time: 5 Minutes

Ingredients:
2 handful of oats
1 handful of quinoa flakes
1 handful of buckwheat flakes
1 tbsp of chopped almonds
1 tbsp of chopped pecans
1 tbsp sunflower seeds
1 tbsp pumpkin seeds
Non-dairy milk of your choice
Pinch of cinnamon
Optional: blueberries, raspberries, strawberries

Instructions:

1   Mix the grains, nuts and seeds together in two bowls and pour in the milk of your choice. I recommend almond milk or hemp milk most strongly, but soy or rice milk are fine too. Finish with a pinch of cinnamon.

2   If you are transitioning, for the first few weeks you can add a few berries.

Nutritional Highlights:

This recipe is beneficial for:

Heart Health
PMS
Liver Health
Energy
Bloating
Muscle Development

Each serve contains the following RDA %'s:

Protein	74%
Vitamin E	132%
Riboflavin	57%
Niacin	25%
Thiamin	72%
Folate	33%
Vitamin B6	25%
Manganese	328%
Magnesium	120%
Calcium	23%
Iron	54%
Potassium	31%
Zinc	50%
Selenium	20%
Fibre	90%

Warm Quinoa Savoury Breakfast

This is fantastic both in summer and winter and gives a filling, protein packed start to the day

Serves: 2
Preparation Time: 20 Minutes

Ingredients:
2 cups of quinoa, prepared
1 avocado
8 cherry tomatoes
2 handfuls of spinach
1 lemon
1 tbsp of sliced almonds
1 inch of fresh ginger
Cayenne pepper
A handful of fresh herbs of your choice
Olive or flax oil
Himalayan salt and pepper

Instructions:

1 Cook the quinoa to the pack instructions and leave aside to cool

2 Slice the avocado, quarter the tomatoes, slice the spinach roughly and crush the ginger in a garlic press.

3 Now construct the meal! Stir the ginger through the quinoa and then create a bed of quinoa. Put the tomato, spinach, avocado and almonds on top of this.

4 Next sprinkle on the cayenne pepper, the herbs of your choice (basil, parsley and coriander work well with this) and squeeze over the lemon juice and drizzle over the flax or olive oil.

5 Season and serve!

Nutritional Highlights:

This recipe is beneficial for:

Energy
Anti-Aging
Immune System
Acne
Weight Loss
Muscle Development

Each serve contains the following RDA %'s:

Protein	56%
Vitamin A	196%
Vitamin C	121%
Vitamin E	110%
Vitamin K	604%
Thiamin	28%
Riboflavin	66%
Vitamin B6	33%
Folate	77%
Calcium	33%
Iron	45%
Magnesium	104%
Potassium	46%
Manganese	190%
Fibre	179%

Oat & Almond Pancakes

Delicious, gluten-free, and just about alkaline!

Serves: 2
Preparation Time: 25 Minutes

Ingredients:
1 1/2 cup gluten-free oat flour
1/4 tsp baking soda
3 tbsp hemp seeds
1 tbsp chia seed
1/2 tsp baking powder
1/2 tsp ground cinnamon
1/4 tsp Himalayan salt (fine)
1 1/2 cups pure water
1/2 cup creamy almond butter
2 tsp vanilla extract
Coconut oil
2 tsp fresh lemon juice
1/2 cup chopped almonds
Pinch of stevia

Instructions:

1. Firstly, mix all of the dry ingredients in a large mixing bowl (preferably glass) - including the oat flour, baking soda, baking powder, stevia, cinnamon and salt.

2. Next, blend the wet stuff! The water, almond butter, vanilla extract and lemon juice to make a kind of almond milk.

3. Mix the In the blender, mix wet ingredients until smooth—you're basically making a fresh, tasty, almost almond milk.

4. Now we need to mix the wet and dry together, so slowly fold in the dry ingredients and then the almonds, hemp and chia seeds. This is your batter complete!

5. Warm your pan and add a little coconut oil. Once it is hot enough, pour your batter in to the size of pancake you want to make. As soon as the bubbles start to appear you know it's time to flip!

6. Once both sides are cooked you're done - stack and move onto the next.

Nutritional Highlights:

This recipe is beneficial for:

Libido
Thyroid
Blood Pressure
Cholesterol
Osteoporosis
Muscle Development

Each serve contains the following RDA %'s:

Protein	39%
Vitamin E	94%
Riboflavin	48%
Niacin	12%
Thiamin	10%
Folate	12%
Manganese	119%
Magnesium	59%
Calcium	43%
Iron	18%
Potassium	25%
Vitamin C	18%
Fibre	60%

Pesto Greens & Scrambled Tofu

Filling, green, protein packed alkaline breakfast

Serves: 2
Preparation Time: 20 Minutes

Ingredients:
1/2 pack silken tofu
8 asparagus spears
Handful of kale
Handful of spinach
1 bulb of bok chi
3 spring onions
6 cherry tomatoes
1 avocado
2 teaspoons of pesto
Bragg liquid aminos
1 clove of garlic, crushed
2 slices of sprouted bread
Himalayan salt and pepper to taste.

Instructions:

1 Start by getting everything washed and prepared. Wash the greens and chop roughly, peel back and wash the spring onions and slice thinly and wash and quarter the cherry tomatoes.

2 To make this dish perfect we need to have two pans on the go at once, so warm a little coconut oil in two different medium sized pans. Put the sprouted bread on to toast now, it takes much longer than normal toast!

3 In one pan, crumble in the silken tofu and add the spring onions, tomatoes and a little splash of Bragg Liquid Aminos (which is an alkaline soy sauce alternative). This needs to be cooked, stirring as needed, for 4-7 minutes

4 In the other pan, once the coconut oil has warmed, throw in all of the greens with the crushed clove of garlic and quickly fry until it's just starting to soften. You want to greens to be al dente.

5 At the last minute add the pesto to the greens and stir through quickly before removing from the heat and serving immediately with the avocado halved and served half per person.

6 Serve with an extra little splash of Bragg and Himalayan salt and pepper to taste.

Nutritional Highlights:

This recipe is beneficial for:

Eczema
Colds & Flu
Constipation
Blood Pressure
Cholesterol
Muscle Development

Each serve contains the following RDA %'s:

Protein	34%
Vitamin K	1177%
Vitamin A	321%
Folate	109%
Thiamin	54%
Vitamin C	194%
Riboflavin	44%
Vitamin E	40%
Niacin	23%
Vitamin B6	48%
Iron	65%
Manganese	70%
Potassium	53%
Magnesium	24%
Fibre	70%

Almost Alkaline Pancakes!

Seed-flour pancakes - a right, proper treat!

Serves: 2
Preparation Time: 30 Minutes

Ingredients:
1/4 cup pumpkin seeds
1/4 cup sunflower seeds
1/4 cup sesame seeds
1/2 cup flax seeds
1 cup of buckwheat, spelt, millet or other healthy flour
1.5 teaspoons of baking soda
1 tsp Himalayan salt
Tiny pinch of stevia
Soy, almond or rice milk
Coconut (or olive) oil

Instructions:

1   Start by making your seed flour. You need to grind in a coffee grinder the four seeds together OR if you can buy pre-ground seeds you can use this (eg. Linseed, Sunflower, Almond mix)

2   Take 1/4 of your seed flour and store the rest for next time.

3   Next mix all of the dry ingredients in a large bowl - the seed flour, buckwheat (or other) flour, baking soda, salt and stevia.

4   Now begin adding the non-dairy milk and stir consistently until you get a thin batter.

5   Next all you need to do is cook them! So heat your pan, add the coconut oil and pour in a thin layer of the batter. When the bubbles appear, flip and serve with whatever you like!

Nutritional Highlights:

This recipe is beneficial for:

Libido
Thyroid
Blood Pressure
Cholesterol
Osteoporosis
Energy

Each serve contains the following RDA %'s:

Protein	19%
Vitamin E	13%
Thiamin	24%
Niacin	20%
Vitamin B6	21%
Folate	12%
Iron	20%
Magnesium	45%
Potassium	10%
Zinc	17%
Manganese	68%
Fibre	27%

Soups

Fennel Soup

This is a highly nutritious and alkalising fennel soup, which will warm you up in these freezing temperatures.

Serves: 2
Preparation Time: 30 Minutes

Ingredients:
2 fennel bulbs
2/8 litre of yeast-free vegetable stock
4 tbsp fresh lemon juice
1/2 tsp Udo's Choice Ultimate Oil Blend or Flax Seed Oil
Ground coriander
Pepper
2 tbsp freshly squeezed orange juice (optional)
1 tsp finely ground orange peel

Instructions:

1   Clean the fennel bulbs, cut out the stalks and shred into very fine pieces. Put a bit of the fennel leaves aside.

2   Bring the vegetable stock together with the lemon juice to boil. Add the fennel and gently cook for about 10-15 minutes until the fennel gets soft. Shortly puree everything with an immersion blender.

3   Season the soup with the oil blend, the ground coriander, pepper and the orange juice.

4   Garnish the soup with the fennel leaves and the orange peel.

Nutritional Highlights:

This recipe is beneficial for:

Heart Health
Immune System
Acne
Digestion
Candida

Each serve contains the following RDA %'s:

Vitamin C	108%
Folate	21%
Vitamin A	25%
Potassium	33%
Manganese	28%
Phosphorous	12%
Calcium	11%
Magnesium	10%
Vitamin K	55%
Dietary Fiber	33%

Courgette and Split Pea Soup

This soup has lovely flavours with a slight hint of spice and will fill and warm you up nicely.

Serves: 4
Preparation Time: 30 Minutes

Ingredients:
1 onion, finely chopped
2 medium courgettes, finely diced
180g/1 cup yellow split peas
1 tsb extra virgin olive oil
900ml yeast-free vegetable stock
1/2 tsp ground turmeric
Himalayan crystal salt
Freshly ground black pepper

Instructions:

1 Put the split peas in a bowl, cover with cold water and leave to soak for a few hours or overnight. Drain, rinse in cold water and drain again.

2 Heat the oil and gently fry the onion in a large covered pot, shaking it occasionally until they are soft. Keep a handful of the diced courgettes by the side and add the rest to the pot. Cook for about 3 minutes whilst stirring.

3 Add the vegetable stock and turmeric and bring to the boil. Reduce the heat, cover with a lid and simmer for about 35 minutes, or until the split peas are tender. Season with salt and pepper to taste.

4 Just before the soup is ready bring a large pot of water to the boil, add the reserved courgettes and cook for about 1 minute. Drain them and add them to the soup.

Nutritional Highlights:

This recipe is beneficial for:

Immune System
Digestion
Blood Pressure
Liver

Each serve contains the following RDA %'s:

Vitamin C	35%
Vitamin B6	11%
Folate	12%
Manganese	12%
Potassium	10%

Alkaline Pistou Soup

Go French with this tasty and healthy soup!

Serves: 4-6
Preparation Time: 40 Minutes

Ingredients:
250g white haricot beans
200g green beans, chopped
2 large garlic cloves, crushed
2 tbsp extra virgin olive oil
1 carrot, finely chopped
1 large onion, finely chopped
1 celery stick, finely chopped
180g new potatoes, cut into cubes
850ml yeast-free vegetable stock
2 tomatoes, skinned and chopped
200g courgettes, diced
1 bunch of basil, finely chopped
Himalayan Crystal Salt & pepper

Ingredients For The Pistou
100g fresh basil leaves
1 1/2 tbsp pine nuts
2 large garlic cloves
50ml extra virgin olive oil

Instructions:

1 Remove the outer skin of the harder and slightly older white beans. To do this carve into the skin with the tip of a knife and push out the inner tender part of the bean.

2 Heat the oil in a large cooking pot at medium temperature, add the onion, garlic, celery and carrot and gently fry for about 5-8 minutes, until the onion is soft, but has not browned.

3 Stir in the potatoes, stock and tomatoes and season with salt and pepper. Bring the broth to boil and add the basil. Reduce the heat, cover the pot with a lid and gently simmer the soup until the potatoes are tender.

4 For the pistou mix the basil, garlic and pine nuts in a mixer until you get a thicker paste. Then add the olive oil. Fill the pistou into bowls, cover them and put them into the fridge until they have to be used later on.

5 As soon as the potatoes are tender, add the courgette, white and green beans to the soup and cook for another 10 minutes until the beans are tender. Season with salt and pepper.

6 Divide the soup into bowls and serve each portion with one large spoonful of pistou.

Nutritional Highlights:

This recipe is beneficial for:

Heart Health
Immune System
Acne
Digestion
PMS

Each serve contains the following RDA %'s:

Vitamin C	50%
Vitamin K	40%
Vitamin B6	18%
Folate	13%
Potassium	15%
Manganese	18%
Vitamin A	49%
Fibre	16%

Alkaline Tomato & Asparagus Soup

Almost raw, and 100% delicious, this is one of the most alkaline recipes I know!

Serves: 2
Preparation Time: 10 Minutes

Ingredients:
10 green asparagus spears
5 tomatoes
2 ripe avocados
1 bunch of fresh parsley
1/4 cup of dried onions
3 garlic cloves
1 red or green pepper
Himalayan salt & black pepper
Optional: fresh herbs (like thyme, rosemary, etc)
2 organic lemons, cut into thin slices

Instructions:

1 Finely puree all ingredients, apart from the lemon slices for garnishing, in a mixer and then gently heat in a large pot.

2 Garnish the soup with the lemon slices. Serve immediately and enjoy!

Nutritional Highlights:

This recipe is beneficial for:

**Immune System
Acne
Digestion
Candida
Colds & Flu**

Each serve contains the following RDA %'s:

Protein	21%
Vitamin K	413%
Vitamin A	74%
Folate	69%
Thiamin	26%
Vitamin C	270%
Vitamin E	27%
Vitamin B6	55%
Iron	26%
Manganese	33%
Potassium	40%
Zinc	13%
Magnesium	19%

Alkaline Gazpacho
Light and Healthy Summer Soup

Serves: 2
Preparation Time: 20 Minutes

Ingredients:
2 red bell Peppers
2 orange bell Peppers
6 vine-ripened tomatoes
1/2 tsp apple cider vinegar
1 tbsp olive oil
1/2 cup avocado diced
1/2 cup cucumber, diced
1/2 cup tomato, diced
Himalayan salt and pepper

Instructions:

1 Char the peppers over a gas flame or under your broiler. They will get very black. Immediately place into a brown paper bag and let steam about 10 minutes.

2 Remove from bag and peel off the skin. Rinse under cold water to remove any more blacken flecks of skin and the seeds and core.

3 Put into a blender. Blend until smooth.

4 Pour into a bowl. Stir in the vinegar and olive oil.

5 To Serve: Pour into bowls and garnish with the avocado, cucumber and tomato. Enjoy.

Nutritional Highlights:

This recipe is beneficial for:

Heart Health
Immune System
Acne
Digestion
PMS

Each serve contains the following RDA %'s:

Vitamin A	81%
Vitamin C	269%
Vitamin E	15%
Vitamin K	38%
Vitamin B6	25%
Folate	26%
Potassium	18%
Manganese	14%
Fibre	29%

Alkaline Courgette Soup

Packed with nutrients and flavour, this is a very simple, but highly alkaline soup

Serves: 2
Preparation Time: 30 Minutes

Ingredients:
6 courgettes
1–2 tablespoons of olive oil
1 chopped onion
2 cloves of garlic
A small bunch of fresh thyme
Salt, pepper and nutmeg
1 liter of vegetable stock

Instructions:

1 In a big pot saute the courgettes, onion , garlic, and thyme in the olive oil. Do it over low flame until the courgettes become slightly golden. Then add salt, pepper and nutmeg, and then add the soup. Cook for 20 mins.

2 Once cooled, put soup in blender and you get the most delicious Cream of Crougettes or Asparagus soup.

Nutritional Highlights:

This recipe is beneficial for:

Eczema
Blood Pressure
Cholesterol
Bad breath
Weight Loss

Each serve contains the following RDA %'s:

Protein	24%
Vitamin C	317%
Vitamin B6	86%
Riboflavin	62%
Folate	57%
Vitamin K	33%
Vitamin A	72%
Thiamin	23%
Niacin	20%
Manganese	105%
Potassium	59%
Magnesium	48%
Iron	63%
Calcium	24%
Fibre	58%

Broccoli Cream Soup

Delicious creamy texture and an awesome mix of herbs

Serves: 2
Preparation Time: 10 Minutes

Ingredients:
2 cups of broccoli
Small handful almonds, soaked
1/2 avocado
1 cup of warm water
1 chopped onion
1-2 cloves garlic
1 tsp dried tarragon
1/2 tsp mint
1 1/2 tsp dill

Instructions:

1 Ensure the almonds have been soaked overnight - if not, don't blend them! You'll have to live without the 'cream' as it's the delicious soaked almonds that give this creamy texture.

2 Steam the brocolli for 5 minutes until it's just, just softening.

3 Put all of the ingredients in a blender together and pulse until smooth, adding water to reach desired consistency.

Nutritional Highlights:

This recipe is beneficial for:

Acne
Digestion
Chronic Fatigue
Bad breath
Weight Loss

Each serve contains the following RDA %'s:

Protein	44%
Vitamin C	177%
Vitamin K	141%
Folate	47%
Vitamin A	20%
Vitamin B6	35%
Riboflavin	50%
Vitamin E	103%
Manganese	114%
Potassium	38%
Magnesium	62%
Calcium	37%
Iron	30%
Fibre	49%

Sweet Potato Soup

Nutritious and incredibly delicious!

Serves: 2
Preparation Time: 30 Minutes

Ingredients:
2 cloves garlic
1 onion, sliced
Two pinches of ground ginger
Two pinches of dried chilli flakes
2 tbsp extra virgin olive oil
400g sweet potatoes, cubed
200ml hot yeast-free vegetable stock
200ml coconut cream
50g fresh coriander leaves
Himalayan Crystal Salt
Freshly ground black pepper
30g spinach leaves, to garnish

Instructions:

1 Heat the oil in a saucepan over a medium heat. Add the garlic and onion and fry for 3-4 minutes, until golden and softened.

2 Add the chilli flakes and ground ginger and fry for one minute, then add the sweet potato and cook for 2-3 minutes.

3 Add the stock and coconut milk. Bring to the boil then reduce the heat to simmer for 8-10 minutes, then add the coriander.

4 Remove from the heat and allow to cool slightly, then pour into a food processor and blend until smooth. Season, to taste, with salt and freshly ground black pepper.

5 To serve, pour the soup into a warm bowl and garnish with the spinach leaves.

Nutritional Highlights:

This recipe is beneficial for:

Kidneys
Liver
Energy
Weight Loss
Bloating

Each serve contains the following RDA %'s:

Protein	13%
Vitamin C	87%
Vitamin K	59%
Niacin	10%
Vitamin B6	45%
Folate	19%
Iron	11%
Magnesium	20%
Potassium	36%
Manganese	33%
Vitamin A	19%
Fibre	25%

Raw Avocado and Tomato Soup
Tasty and Refreshing - You'll Love This!

Serves: 2
Preparation Time: 15 Minutes

Ingredients:
3 avocados
3 tomatoes
2 handfuls of fresh spinach
2 tsp freshly squeezed lemon
A pinch of Himalayan Crystal
Freshly ground pepper
A small amount of water
(depending on how liquid you like
the soup to be)

Instructions:

1   Cut the tomatoes into small pieces.

2   Put all the ingredients apart from the tomato pieces into a blender
    and blend until smooth.

3   Pour the soup into a soup bowl and add the tomato pieces and,
    optinally, serve with a slice of toasted sprouted bread, topped
    with the Red Pepper Dip and some alfalfa sprouts.

Nutritional Highlights:

This recipe is beneficial for:

IBS
Candida
Eczema
Colds & Flu
Constipation

Each serve contains the
following RDA %'s:

Protein	17%
Vitamin K	391%
Folate	86%
Vitamin C	111%
Vitamin B6	44%
Vitamin E	37%
Vitamin A	118%
Potassium	50%
Copper	32%
Magnesium	33%
Iron	17%
Fibre	91%

Moroccan Vegetable Soup

The creamy parsnip and pumpkin give this soup a wonderfully rich texture!

Serves: 4
Preparation Time: 30 Minutes

Ingredients:
30ml/2 tbsp olive or coconut oil
1 onion, chopped
225g carrots, chopped
225g parsnips, chopped
225g pumpkin
900ml of vegetable stock
Lemon juice, to taste
Himalayan Salt and black pepper

For The Garnish (Optional):
7.5ml/1 1/2 tbsp olive oil
1/2 garlic clove, finely chopped
3 tbsp chopped fresh parsley and
coriander, mixed
A good pinch of paprika

Instructions:

1 Heat the oil in a large pan and fry the onion for about 3 minutes until softened, stirring occasionally. Add the carrots and parsnips, stir well, cover and cook over a low heat for a further 5 minutes.

2 Cut the pumpkin into chunks, discarding the skin and pith, and stir into the pan. Cover and cook for another 5 minutes. Add the stock and seasoning, and slowly bring to the boil. Cover the pan and simmer very gently for 35-40 minutes until all the vegetables are tender.

3 After the soup has slightly cooled, puree it with a food blender or in a food processor until smooth. If the texture is too thick for your liking you can just add a little extra water. Reheat the soup if necessary. Stir in lemon juice to taste.

4 To make the garnish, heat the oil in a small pan and add the garlic, parsley and coriander. Fry gently for 1-2 minutes. Add the paprika and stir well.

Pour into bowls and spoon a little garnish on top.

Nutritional Highlights:

This recipe is beneficial for:

Candida
Eczema
Colds & Flu
Digestion
Acne

Each serve contains the following RDA %'s:

Vitamin C	19%
Vitamin K	10%
Potassium	10%
Manganese	13%
Vitamin A	88%

Leeks and Asparagus Soup

I hope you enjoy this delicious alkalising leeks and asparagus soup, which has a lovely lemon tang!

Serves: 4
Preparation Time: 30 Minutes

Ingredients:
800g fresh green asparagus
3 leeks, peeled and chopped
1/2 lemon
2 tbsp Olive Oil or Udo's Choice Ultimate Oil Blend
4 mugs of vegetable stock
Himalayan crystal salt
Freshly ground pepper

Instructions:

1 Wash the asparagus and chop off the woody ends of the stems. Cut off the asparagus tips and keep to one side, as you will need to use them later on. Chop up the asparagus stalks.

2 Add 2 tbsp of oil into a large saucepan and gently fry the leeks for about 10-15 minutes until they start to soften. Add the stock and chopped up asparagus stalks and simmer with a lid on for about 25 minutes.

3 Remove the soup from the heat and blend in a food processor or with a hand-held blender.

4 Season the soup to taste, add the asparagus tips and bring the soup back to the boil. Cook the soup on a very low heat for another 5 minutes until the tips have softened. Add fresh lemon juice.

Nutritional Highlights:

This recipe is beneficial for:

Immune System
Acne
Digestion
Candida
Eczema

Each serve contains the following RDA %'s:

Vitamin K	28%
Vitamin A	12%
Vitamin C	25%
Vitamin E	3%
Vitamin B6	5%
Iron	6%
Copper	6%
Manganese	8%
Fibre	6%

Carrot & Artichoke Soup

The main star in this delicious and alkaline soup - Jerusalem Artichokes

Serves: 6-8 people
Preparation Time: 30 Minutes

Ingredients:
700g Jerusalem artichokes
3 celery stalks, chopped
450g carrots
1 medium onion, chopped
3 tbsp olive oil
1.5 litres yeast-free vegetable stock
Himalayan crystal salt
Freshly ground pepper

Instructions:

1   Peel and slice the artichokes, then put them into a bowl of cold water to prevent them from discolouring. Peel and slice the carrots.

2   Gently heat the olive oil in a cooking pot and soften the onion and celery for ca. 5 minutes, then stir in the carrots and artichokes. Add a pinch of salt, put the lid on and let the vegetables sweat for ca. 10 minutes on a low heat.

3   Then pour in the stock, stir well, put the lid back on and simmer for a further 20 minutes or until the vegetables are soft. Then liquidise the soup.

4   Taste to check the seasoning, re-heat and serve!

Nutritional Highlights:

This recipe is beneficial for:

PMS
Kidney
Liver
Energy
Osteoporosis

Each serve contains the following RDA %'s:

Vitamin C	10%
Thiamin	13%
Iron	17%
Potassium	13%
Vitamin A	27%

Super Hearty Minestrone

Fast, filling and full of goodness

Serves: 2
Preparation Time: 20-30 Minutes

Ingredients:
1/2 cup of eggplant (aubergine)
1/2 cup of sweet potato
1/2 cup of zucchini (courgette)
1/2 cup of carrot
1/4 red onion
2 cloves of garlic
1/2 cup of beans
1 tbsp coconut oil
1 cup of vegetable stock
1 handful of basil
1 cup of tomato juice (fresh or bought)
Himalayan salt & black pepper

Instructions:

1 Wash and cube the aubergine, potato and courgette and dice the carrot and onion.

2 In a large pot, gently sauté these ingredients in the coconut oil for about 2 minutes.

3 Now add the beans (can be any bean you like) and add the stock and tomato juice - bring this to a boil and then lower the heat to simmer for just 8-10 minutes.

4 Stir in the basil and season to taste

Nutritional Highlights:

This recipe is beneficial for:

Bloating
Weight Loss
Liver
Kidneys
PMS

Each serve contains the following RDA %'s:

Folate	16%
Vitamin K	84%
Vitamin B6	16%
Vitamin C	32%
Manganese	41%
Potassium	20%
Copper	13%
Magnesium	12%
Vitamin A	161%
Fibre	30%

Mexican Tortilla Soup
Satisfy your craving for Mexican - the Alkaline Way!

Serves: 4
Preparation Time: 30 Minutes

Ingredients:
500ml of (alkaline) water
2 teaspoons of vegetable bouillon
or 1 yeast-free stock cube
1 ripe avocado
1/2 red capsicum (pepper)
1 tomato
1/2 bunch of coriander (cilantro)
2 large handfuls of spinach
2 cloves of garlic
1 lime
1 corn on the cob (about 4in long)
1 chili/jalapeno (to your taste)
Black pepper and Himalayan Salt
1 sprouted tortilla wrap

Instructions:

1 Firstly, get your tortilla ready by slicing into 1cm wide and 5cm long strips and lightly toasting under the grill.

2 Now prepare the base by simply boiling the alkaline water in a large pan and dissolve the stock cubes/bouillon to make a vegetable broth as a base.

3 Next, get the veggies ready by dicing the capsicum and tomato and roughly chopping the coriander. Now peel and dice the avocado and finely dice or mince the garlic. Next, slice up the chili/jalepeno to your hotness preference and put to one side. Wash and roughly chop your delicious super-alkaline spinach and dry with a tea towel.

4 Now finally prepare the corn by slicing the kernels from the cob with a sharp knife.

5 All that is left is to combine everything into the broth – so simply throw it all together and heat through. You may choose to keep the tomato and chili to one side and throw in right at the end so that it stays quite raw.

Nutritional Highlights:

This recipe is beneficial for:

Heart Health
Digestion
Eczema
Blood Pressure
Cholesterol

Each serve contains the following RDA %'s:

Vitamin K	332%
Folate	38%
Vitamin C	84%
Vitamin B6	19%
Vitamin E	12%
Vitamin A	112%
Potassium	18%
Magnesium	15%
Manganese	31%
Fibre	26%

Ribollita Vegetable Bean Soup

A famous soup from Tuscany, Italy - Buon Appetito!

Serves 4 as a starter
Serves 2 as a main course
Preparation Time: 60 Minutes

Ingredients:
250g of green vegetables
1 carrot
1 celery stick
2-3 garlic cloves
60g of sprouted bread (or healthiest alternative)
1-2 rosemary twigs
4 tbsp olive oil
1 litre of yeast-free vegetable stock
1 can of precooked white beans
1 red onion
Himalayan Salt and black pepper

Instructions:

1 Wash the green vegtables and roughly cut them into pieces. Peel the carrot, wash the celery stick and cut both into strips and then small cube-size pieces. Peel the garlic cloves and cut them into very fine pieces. Cut the sprouted bread into cube-size pieces. Wash the rosemary twigs, take off the needles and cut them into small pieces.

2 Gently heat 1 tbsp of the oil in a large pot. Add the carrot, celery and garlic and fry them very briefly in the oil. Stir in the rest of the vegetables together with the rosemary.

3 Add the bread and stock and let it heat up. Reduce the heat to medium level and cover the pot with a lid. Cook the vegetables for about 15 minutes until they start to soften.

4 Drain the canned beans in a colander and let cold water run over them, until all the liquid from the can has fully drained. Add the beans to the soup and let it cook for about 25 minutes whilst stirring occasionally. The aim is for the soup to thicken! Try the soup and season to taste with salt and pepper.

5 You have two options now: either leave the soup to cool down and gently reheat the next day as the Italians do or peel the onion straight after cooking, halve and cut it into very fine strips. Put the onion strips onto a small plate and put the pot of soup straight onto the dinning table. Take as much Ribollita as you like, sprinkle over the onion strips and drizzle over some olive oil.

Nutritional Highlights:

This recipe is beneficial for:

Heart Health
Immune System
Acne
Digestion
PMS

Each serve contains the following RDA %'s:

Protein	13%
Vitamin A	60%
Vitamin C	33%
Vitamin K	19%
Vitamin B6	13%
Potassium	16%
Manganese	29%
Folate	19%
Iron	15%
Magnesium	12%
Copper	10%
Fibre	22%

Tunisian Chickpea Soup

This warming and alkalising chickpea soup has got delicious Arabic flavours.

Serves: 4
Preparation Time: 30 Minutes

Ingredients:
350g dried chickpeas, soaked in cold water overnight and drained
10 garlic cloves, cut fine
2 1/2 litres of water
8 tbsp extra virgin olive oil
2 carrots, cut into fine strips
5 celery stalks, cut into thin rings
2 onions, very finely chopped
1 tsp ground cumin
1 tsp ground coriander
4 tbsp finely chopped coriander
Juice of one lemon
Himalayan salt and black pepper

Instructions:

1 Gently heat half of the olive oil in a big pot. Add the garlic and steam for about two minutes. Add the chickpeas, water, cumin and ground coriander. Bring all ingredients to the boil. Reduce the heat and simmer for about 2 1/2 hours.

2 In the meantime heat the remaining oil in a frying pan, add the carrots, onions and celery. Gently fry whilst stirring.

3 Add the vegetables to the soup and stir in well. Take about half of the soup and puree in a mixer or with a hand held mixer. Add the puree to the soup and stir well. Spice the soup with salt and pepper and the lemon juice.

4 Fill the soup into pre-warmed bowls and garnish the soup with the fresh coriander.

Nutritional Highlights:

This recipe is beneficial for:

Digestion
IBS
Candida
Constipation
Blood Pressure

Each serve contains the following RDA %'s:

Protein	11%
Vitamin B6	35%
Folate	21%
Vitamin C	26%
Manganese	32%
Phosphorous	10%
Copper	10%
Vitamin A	117%
Vitamin K	51%
Potassium	10%
Fibre	22%

Salads

Pearl Barley Salad

A filling salad inspired by my trip to Turkey!

Serves: 2
Preparation Time: 10 Minutes

Ingredients:
1/3 cup pearl barley
1/4 cup green lentil
1/2 red pepper, chopped
2 green onions, sliced
1/2 green pepper, chopped
2 fresh mint leaves, torn
1 tsp basil
2 tbsp lemon juice
2 tbsp pomegranate paste or 1 fresh pomegranate
1/4 cup extra virgin olive oil
Himalayan salt and pepper

Instructions:

1 Prepare the barley and lentils according to the pack instructions (or just the barley if you're using tinned lentils, which is fine).

2 Prepare the veggies and juices and oils and toss everything in a bowl together.

3 For the best result, cool in a fridge for an hour, but if you're short on time, it's fine to eat immediately.

Nutritional Highlights:

This recipe is beneficial for:

Digestion
IBS
Candida
Constipation
Blood Pressure

Each serve contains the following RDA %'s:

Protein	17%
Vitamin K	7256%
Niacin	10%
Vitamin B6	35%
Folate	34%
Calcium	14%
Iron	19%
Magnesium	19%
Potassium	19%
Manganese	56%
Vitamin C	163%
Vitamin A	49%
Fibre	38%

Cool Quinoa Summer Salad
Wicked Cool - Ross's Personal Favorite!

Serves: 2
Preparation Time: 30 Minutes

Ingredients:
15 cherry tomatoes
1 serve of quinoa
1 carrot
1 avocado
1 beetroot
A handful of baby peas
A handful of basil
A good pinch of sage leaves
A pinch of Himalayan salt
A pinch of black pepper
Dressing of olive oil with lemon juice

Instructions:

1 Firstly, get the quinoa cooked and out of the way. The rough guide is to mix one part quinoa to five parts water, so do this (unless you pack says otherwise), bring to a boil and then simmer super-gently until the water has absorbed.

2 Next, you have two options with the beetroot and carrot. If you have a Spiral Slicer use this to make carrot and beetroot spirals, but if not then you will want to grate them with a standard cheese grater into a bowl. Once grated, press with some kitchen roll/ towel to get rid of some of the excess moisture.

3 While you're spiralising or grating have the baby peas steaming gently for a few minutes to cook through and then put aside.

4 Slice or dice your avocado as you like and then mix all of this into a large bowl with the herbs (which you can roughly chop or rip) and set it all aside while you sort out yer' tomatoes!

5 Now, you're going to be grilling the tomatoes (surprise!) so chop them in half and drizzle with olive oil and place under the grill for about 5 minutes until they start to just blacken and are warmed.

6 With the tomatoes done you can mix it all up into a big bowl and dress with the olive oil and lemon juice.

Nutritional Highlights:

This recipe is beneficial for:

Immune System
Acne
Digestion
Candida
Colds & Flu

Each serve contains the following RDA %'s:

Vitamin K	123%
Vitamin A	234%
Vitamin C	24%
Folate	10%
Sodium	11%
Manganese	22%
Fibre	10%

Roast Garlic and Spinach Salad

I love the crunchy texture of the spinach and the sweet taste of the roast garlic in this alkalising salad.

Serves: 4
Preparation Time: 30 Minutes

Ingredients:
500g baby spinach leaves
10 garlic cloves, unpeeled
40g pine nuts, lightly toasted
Fresh juice of 1/2 lemon
4 tbsp extra virgin olive oil
Himalayan salt
Freshly ground black pepper

Instructions:

1 Preheat your oven to about 180 Celsius. Put the garlic cloves into a roasting dish, toss in about 2 tbsp of the oil and bake for about 10-15 minutes until the garlic cloves have turned slightly golden and have started to soften.

2 Tip the garlic into a salad bowl. Add the lemon juice, pine nuts, spinach, remaining olive oil and season to taste.

3 Mix well and serve immediately.

   TIP: Try to squeeze the garlic puree out ... it's delicious!

Nutritional Highlights:

This recipe is beneficial for:

Heart Health
Weight Loss
Immune System
Anti-Aging
Acne
Libido

Each serve contains the following RDA %'s:

Protein: 4%		0%
Vitamin B6: 12%		2%
Vitamin C:10%		10%
Manganese: 2%		2%
Fibre: 11%		1%

Alkaline Quinoa Salad with Avocado
Delicious and Refreshing Salad - Perfect as a Side Dish or Main Dish

Serves: 2
Preparation Time: 30 Minutes

Ingredients:
1 cucumber, diced
1 avocado, quartered
3 roma tomatoes, chopped
1 small red onion, finely chopped
1 1/2 cups quinoa
4 radishes
1/4 cup extra virgin olive oil
3 tbs fresh lemon juice
2 tsp grated lemon zest
1 handful fresh parsley, chopped
Himalayan crystal salt
Freshly ground black pepper

Instructions:

1 Bring about 2 litres salted water to a boil. Add the quinoa, cover the pot, and reduce the heat to medium-low. Simmer for about 14 minutes, or until quinoa is tender. You know this when small "tails" bloom from grains.

2 Preheat the oven to 200 Celsius. Spread the pine nuts on a baking tray and toast them in the oven until lightly browned. This will take about 3 to 4 minutes. Cool afterwards and put into a large serving bowl.

3 Drain the quinoa and rinse it under cool running water. Drain again. Add the quinoa to the pine nuts and stir in the onion, tomatoes, cucumber and parsley.

4 Drizzle over the olive oil, lemon zest and juice. Season with salt and pepper. To garnish place the avocado quarters over the salad.

Nutritional Highlights:

This recipe is beneficial for:

Kidneys
Liver
Energy
Weight Loss
Bloating

Each serve contains the following RDA %'s:

Protein	17%
Vitamin K	58%
Vitamin C	55%
Vitamin B6	22%
Folate	42%
Thiamin	18%
Potassium	31%
Manganese	49%
Magnesium	31%
Iron	16%
Zinc	13%
Vitamin E	14%
Dietary Fiber	44%

Warm Broccoli Salad

Warming and reassuring salad for a cold day!

Serves: 2
Preparation Time: 20 Minutes

Ingredients:
400g fresh broccoli, chopped
1 onion, cut into small pieces
100g cherry tomatoes, chopped
Fresh juice of one lemon
2 tbsp fresh parsley, chopped up
2 tsp dried oregano and thyme
1 tbsp olive oil or Udo's Choice
Himalayan crystal salt and freshly
ground pepper to taste

Instructions:

1   Cut all ingredients into small pieces as stated above.

2   Steam the broccoli florets very shortly in a frying pan until they
    get a very nice green colour. Make sure the florets still have a
    crunchy texture.

3   Put all the vegetables into a salad bowl. Pour over the fresh
    lemon juice and olive oil, add the herbs and season with salt and
    pepper. Mix everything together and add some more seasoning if
    needed.

Nutritional Highlights:

This recipe is beneficial for:

Bad Breath
PMS
Weight Loss
Bloating
Kidneys

Each serve contains the
following RDA %'s:

Protein	14%
Vitamin A	48%
Vitamin C	348%
Vitamin K	541%
Riboflavin	14%
Vitamin B6	22%
Folate	40%
Calcium	12%
Iron	13%
Magnesium	10%
Potassium	23%
Manganese	24%
Fiber	28%

Mixed Avocado Salad

Light and healthy dish, ideal for lunch or dinner time

Serves: 2
Preparation Time: 20 Minutes

Ingredients:
1 large avocado
1 tomato
2 handfuls of fresh spinach
2 handfuls of fresh rocket
2 grated carrots
1 small garlic clove
1 small onion
10-12 almonds
2 tbsp extra virgin olive oil
Freshly squeezed juice of 1 lime
Freshly ground pepper
Optional: Himalayan crystal salt or celtic sea salt

Instructions:

1 Thoroughly wash and drain the green lettuce and spinach and put into a big salad bowl. Peel and grate the carrots, add them to the salad bowl, thoroughly mix up all the ingredients and put bowl to the side.

2 Cut the avocado, onion, garlic and tomato into small pieces. Put all the pieces into a seperate wooden bowl and mix all the ingredients together. Mash up all the ingredients with the help of a fork until it all becomes like a puree. Add 2 tbsps of olive oil and the lime juice and mix it all together.

3 Put the avocado puree over the spinach, carrots and green lettuce. Chop up the almonds into small pieces, add them to the salad and mix up all the ingredients.

4 Season the salad to taste and enjoy every bite of this delicious and highly alkalising avocado salad!

Nutritional Highlights:

This recipe is beneficial for:

Heart Health
Acne
Digestion
IBS
Candida

Each serve contains the following RDA %'s:

Protein	24%
Vitamin A	553%
Vitamin C	120%
Vitamin E	44%
Vitamin K	864%
Riboflavin	27%
Vitamin B6	38%
Folate	87%
Calcium	19%
Iron	27%
Magnesium	40%
Potassium	52%
Fiber	64%

Mixed Chick Pea Salad With Avocado and Lemon Dressing

Light crunchy salad with a very unique dressing!

Serves: 2
Preparation Time: 20 Minutes

Ingredients:
400g fresh chickpeas (cooked)
1 big bag of fresh spinach leaves
3 tomatoes
100 g green asparagus
1 red or green pepper
2 spring onions

For the avocado dressing
1 avocado
Juice of one lemon
Cold-pressed olive oil or Udo's
Choice Ultimate Oil Blend
Himalayan salt and black pepper

Instructions:

1 Start by very lightly steaming the asparagus.

2 Cut up all ingredients, apart from the avocado, into small pieces, put them into a salad bowl and mix everything together.

3 Peel the avocado and cut into small pieces. Add the avocado pieces together with the lemon juice and a little bit of oil into a mixer. Briefly mix the ingredients until you get a slightly thick dressing.

4 Add the avocado salad dressing together with a pinch of salt over the salad and mix everything together.

Enjoy this delicious alkaline salad!

Nutritional Highlights:

This recipe is beneficial for:

Eczema
Colds & Flu
Constipation
Blood Pressure
Cholesterol

Each serve contains the following RDA %'s:

Protein	22%
Vitamin B6	43%
Folate	59%
Vitamin C	150%
Riboflavin	15%
Manganese	67%
Sodium	15%
Iron	27%
Magnesium	21%
Calcium	13%
Vitamin A	131%
Vitamin K	472%
Potassium	15%
Fibre	43%

Avocado Summer Mexican Salad

Bring some summer to your table - Try this dish!

Serves: 2
Preparation Time: 40 Minutes

Ingredients:
2 Wraps/Tortillas – preferably
sprouted or yeast/gluten free
1/2 pack of firm tofu, cooked
1 avocado
150g black beans
150g quinoa
1 pink grapefruit
A handful of almonds
4 handfuls of baby spinach
1 spoon of chilli sauce
2 tomatoes
1/2 red onion
1/2 lemon

Instructions:

1 Firstly, get the tortilla bowls ready by preheating the oven to about 180 degrees celsius. Once it has preheated, place the wraps over a medium bowl, push them in slightly and then bake for 8-10 minutes until they've formed a bowl shape and crisped up a little. Once they're done place to one side and cool.

2 While this is cooling, prepare the quinoa to the packet instructions.

3 Chop up the tofu, onion and tomatoes and mix with the chilli sauce and then place in the fridge for 10 mins to cool a little. While this is cooling, finely chop the almonds and peel and slice the avocado and grapefruit.

4 Now mix it all together, place in the bowl and top with the spinach before squeezing the fresh lemon on top. Delicious!

Nutritional Highlights:

This recipe is beneficial for:

Eczema
Blood Pressure
Cholesterol
Bad breath
Weight Loss

Each serve contains the following RDA %'s:

Protein	44%
Vitamin K	33%
Folate	37%
Vitamin C	103%
Vitamin B6	25%
Vitamin E	104%
Vitamin A	27%
Potassium	37%
Copper	53%
Magnesium	61%
Iron	22%
Riboflavin	43%
Calcium	23%
Fibre	44%

Kohlrabi Salad with Vegetable Dressing

An Excellent Source of Vitamin C, Magnesium and Phosphorous - Guten Appetit!

Serves: 2
Preparation Time: 15 Minutes

Ingredients:
3 green kohlrabi
1 spring onion or shallot
4 tbsp fresh sprouts
3 tbsp olive oil or Udo's Choice
Fresh juice of half a lemon
Himalayan Crystal Salt
Freshly ground black pepper

Instructions:

1   Cut the spring onion or shallot into small pieces. Prepare a dressing out of the oil, lemon juice, salt, pepper and sprouts and mix in the finely cut onion.

2   Peel the kohlrabi and cut into very thin slices. Lay the kohlrabi slices onto a big plate and cover with the dressing.

Nutritional Highlights:

This recipe is beneficial for:

Immune System
Digestion
Eczema
Colds & Flu
Blood Pressure

Each serve contains the following RDA %'s:

Protein	6%
Vitamin A	10%
Vitamin C	117%
Vitamin K	136%
Folate	8%
Calcium	7%
Iron	4%
Potassium	4%
Fibre	21%

Lamb's Lettuce with Walnuts and Avocado
A Light and Tasty Alkaline Snack

Serves: 2
Preparation Time: 15 Minutes

Ingredients:
1 lamb's lettuce (or other leaves)
200g of walnuts
1 bunch of fresh chives and parsley
2 avocados
Lemon juice of 1 lemon
4 tbsp walnut oil, cold-pressed
olive oil or Udo's Choice Celtic
Himalayan crystal salt
Freshly ground black pepper

Instructions:

1 Wash the lamb's lettuce, open the walnuts and halve them. Cut the avocado in small pieces, wash the chives and cut into little rolls.

2 Prepare the dressing by mixing together the olive oil, fresh lemon juice and fresh herbs. Season with salt and pepper to taste.

3 Add the dressing to the salad.

Nutritional Highlights:

This recipe is beneficial for:

Digestion
IBS
Candida
Constipation
Blood Pressure

Each serve contains the following RDA %'s:

Protein	27%
Vitamin K	90%
Folate	59%
Vitamin C	65%
Vitamin B6	42%
Vitamin E	21%
Thiamine	23%
Vitamin A	18%
Potassium	36%
Magnesium	38%
Manganese	117%
Iron	16%
Fibre	72%

Carrot, Broccoli and Bean Shoot Salad

Raw, Alkaline Goodness with a Zingy, Delicious Dressing!

Serves: 2
Preparation Time: 20 Minutes

Ingredients:
3 cups carrots, shredded
2 cups broccoli slaw or finely julienned broccoli stalks
2 cups mung been shoots
1 large cucumber, peeled, julienned
2 cups fresh coriander, chopped finely
1 bunch green onions, sliced finely

For the dressing
1/2 cup freshly squeezed lime juice
1 tablespoon of Bragg Liquid Aminos or Soy Sauce if transitioning
3 tablespoons sesame oil
1 crushed garlic clove
1 deseeded red chili

Instructions:

1 Toss all of the vegetables together with the coriander.

2 Place all of the dressing ingredients, except the chili and garlic, in your blender and pulse a few times until well combined. Stir in the garlic and chili.

3 Pour the dressing over the salad and season, to taste.

4 Garnish with sesame seeds or chopped raw nuts if desired.

Nutritional Highlights:

This recipe is beneficial for:

Heart Health
Anti-Aging
Weight Loss
Blood Pressure

Each serve contains the following RDA %'s:

Protein	6%
Vitamin A	16%
Vitamin C	117%
Vitamin K	136%
Riboflavin	13%
Potassium	23%
Calcium	17%
Iron	14%
Magnesium	23%
Fibre	21%
Manganese	4%
Vitamin B6	3%

Mixed Sprouts Salad
Crunchy, Super Delicious and Alkalizing Salad

Serves: 2
Preparation Time: 15 Minutes

Ingredients:
A mixture of sprouts of your choice
(e.g. radish, alfalfa and cress)
1 cucumber
1 spring onion
A handful of fresh chives, dill and
parsley
1 or 2 tbsp coconut oil or Udo's
Choice Ultimate Oil Blend
Fresh juice of half a lemon
Himalayan Crystal Salt
Freshly ground black pepper

Instructions:

1 Chop up all the herbs into small pieces. Prepare a dressing out
   of the herbs, oil, lemon juice, salt and pepper.

2 Cut the spring onion and cucumber into small pieces and add to
   the dressing.

3 Wash and drain the sprouts and mix them with the dressing.

Nutritional Highlights:

This recipe is beneficial for:

Acne
Digestion
Candida
Cholesterol
Osteoporosis

Each serve contains the
following RDA %'s:

Vitamin K	204%
Vitamin C	39%
Vitamin A	25%
Folate	14%
Potassium	11%
Manganese	13%
Dietary Fiber	11%

Radicchio, Artichoke & Walnut Salad

Light and crunchy - a great snack!

Serves 2
Preparation Time: 20 Minutes

Ingredients:
1 large radicchio
40g/6 tbsp walnut pieces
45ml/3 tbsp walnut oil
500g Jerusalem artichokes
Juice and pared rind of 1 lemon
Himalayan crystal salt
Freshly ground black pepper
Optional: flat leaf parsley, to garnish

Instructions:

1 If you are using a whole radicchio, cut it into 8-10 wedges. Put the wedges or leaves in a flameproof dish. Scatter over the walnuts, then drizzle over the oil and season. Grill for 2-3 minutes.

2 Peel the artichokes and cut up any large ones so the pieces are all roughly the same size. Add the artichokes to a pan of boiling salted water with half the lemon juice and cook for 5-7 minutes until tender. Drain. Preheat the grill to high.

3 Toss the artichokes into the salad with the remaining lemon juice and the pared rind. Season with salt and pepper. Grill until beginning to brown. Serve at once garnished with torn pieces of parsley, if you like.

Nutritional Highlights:

This recipe is beneficial for:

Heart Health
Immune System
Digestion
IBS
Candida

Each serve contains the following RDA %'s:

Protein	21%
Thiamin	20%
Vitamin B6	16%
Folate	15%
Iron	19%
Magnesium	23%
Phosphorus	24%
Potassium	14%
Zinc	12%
Copper	53%
Manganese	100%
Vitamin K	45%
Fibre	19%

Mexican Corn Salsa Salad

Packed with nutrients and perfect for a hot, summer's day

Serves: 2
Preparation Time: 20 Minutes

Ingredients:
2 large corn on the cobs
2 carrots
2 small peppers, one red, one yellow
2 spring onions (scallions)
2 red chilies (vary this depending on how hot you like it)
1 avocado
Juice of 1 ½ limes

Instructions:

1 Hold the corn on the cob vertically and run a sharp knife down their sides to remove the corn. Put the corn into your serving bowl.

2 Grate the carrots and add them to the corn.

3 Dice the peppers into small pieces and add to the corn and carrot.

4 Chop the spring onion into small slices and add to the vegetables.

5 Put rubber gloves on and slice the chillies lengthways. Remove the pips. Chop into very small pieces – take your time over this, especially if the chillies are hot, the dish will have a much more rounded flavour if you can make the pieces as small as possible. Add the chilli to the vegetable mixture.

6 Scoop out the avocado flesh and put it in a second bowl.

7 Juice the lime and pour over the avocado.

8 Mash the avocado and lime together with a fork until smooth.

9 Put the avocado dressing on top of the vegetables in the serving bowl and mix really well.

Nutritional Highlights:

This recipe is beneficial for:

IBS
Candida
Immune System
Heart Health
Acne

Each serve contains the following RDA %'s:

Protein	17%
Vitamin B6	52%
Thiamin	12%
Vitamin C	578%
Niacin	12%
Folate	47%
Magnesium	18%
Potassium	38%
Manganese	28%
Vitamin A	267%
Vitamin K	178%
Iron	10%
Copper	15%
Vitamin E	15%
Fibre	63%

79

Warm Red Pepper, Spinach & Courgette Salad

Mediterranean Style Salad at its Best

Serves: 2
Preparation Time: 60 Minutes

Ingredients:
1 red pepper, de-seeded
250 g courgettes
300 g fresh baby spinach
100g fresh watercress,
150 ml extra virgin olive oil
Himalayan crystal salt
Freshly ground pepper
1/2 lemon, juiced to dress

Instructions:

1 Wash and drain all the vegetables. Cut the courgettes into thin slices. Dry the spinach leaves amd watercress and lay them in a shallow serving dish.

2 Place the olive oil into a wide oven-proof dish over low heat. Add the courgettes and peppers and season with salt and pepper according to taste. Cover the casserole dish and cook gently for about 30 minutes or until the vegetables are tender.

3 Remove from the oven and serve on top of the leaves, and dress with olive oil and the lemon juice. The courgettes should be tender but still have their colour.

Nutritional Highlights:

This recipe is beneficial for:

Heart Health
Immune System
Acne
Digestion
Candida

Each serve contains the following RDA %'s:

Vitamin C	158%
Vitamin B6	21%
Riboflavin	11%
Folate	14%
Vitamin K	14%
Vitamin A	144%
Manganese	14%
Potassium	14%
Fibre	15%

Rocket, Watercress and Mint Salad

A great recipe to get 2-3 serves of greens in your body with very little effort!

Serves: 2
Preparation Time: 10 Minutes

Ingredients:
100g rocket (also known as arugula)
100g watercress
100g chickpeas
1/2 bunch of fresh mint
2tbsp of olive oil
2tbsp fresh lemon juice
Himalayan salt and ground pepper

Instructions:

1 Wash the leaves and dry them. Arrange them in a bowl and toss through the chickpeas. Sprinkle the mint on top and then add the dressing, salt and pepper and enjoy!

Nutritional Highlights:

This recipe is beneficial for:

Heart Health
Candida
Eczema
Colds & Flu
Chronic Fatigue

Each serve contains the following RDA %'s:

Protein	18%
Vitamin A	68%
Vitamin C	82%
Vitamin K	224%
Folate	36%
Calcium	18%
Iron	17%
Magnesium	20%
Phosphorus	17%
Potassium	13%
Manganese	58%
Vitamin B6	32%
Sodium	15%
Fibre	30%

Lunch

Chickpea Patties with Tomato, Cucumber & Mint Salad

A fantastic dinnertime treat for the whole family

Serves: 2
Preparation Time: 1 Hour 15 Minutes

Ingredients:
2 sweet potatoes
1 can of chickpeas
2 cloves of garlic, crushed
3 spring onions
Handful of chopped coriander
1 tablespoon of polenta
1 cucumber
2 tomatoes
1/2 fresh lime, juiced
1 tbsp of pumpkin seeds
1 tbsp of sesame seeds
1/2 cup of soy yoghurt
1 handful of fresh mint
Coconut or olive oil

Instructions:

1   Peel and steam the sweet potato until tender and then mash this with the chickpeas in a bowl.

2   Add the garlic, crushed, the onion, sliced and the coriander, roughly chopped.

3   Shape this mixture into little patties (burgers) and coat in the polenta. Once you're all done, refrigerate for one hour. As the hour approaches, turn on the oven to 180 degrees to preheat.

4   While these are cooling, prepare the salad by slicing the cucumber and the tomatoes and mixing in a bowl with the seeds, juice and mint. Once combined, stir through the soy yoghurt and season.

5   Now the patties are cooled, warm a medium pan with a little coconut or olive oil and lightly cook until browned very slightly.

6   Now transfer to the oven to cook through and then serve with the salad and dressing. Yum!

Nutritional Highlights:

This recipe is beneficial for:

Heart Health
Immune System
Acne
Digestion
PMS

Each serve contains the following RDA %'s:

Protein	36%
Vitamin K	230%
Vitamin C	81%
Vitamin A	423%
Riboflavin	16%
Vitamin B6	54%
Folate	40%
Potassium	31%
Manganese	116%
Magnesium	58%
Iron	43%
Calcium	27%
Sodium	15%
Dietary Fiber	76%

Courgette Delight

So quick and easy to make and surprisingly filling!

Serves: 2
Preparation Time: 15 Minutes

Ingredients:
1/2 bunch of spring onions,
chopped
1 garlic clove, crushed
2 courgettes, sliced or made into
ribbons
1 tbsp sliced almonds
Olive oil
Himalayan salt and pepper

Instructions:

1   Start by warming the garlic and onion in a pan on a very low heat with the olive oil until fragrant

2   Prepare the courgette either by slicing or using a vegetable peeler to make ribbons and then add this to the pan.

3   As soon as the courgette is softening throw in the almonds and remove from the heat and season to taste.

Nutritional Highlights:

This recipe is beneficial for:

Kidneys
Liver
Energy
Weight Loss
Bloating

Each serve contains the following RDA %'s:

Protein	38%
Vitamin C	74%
Vitamin B6	29%
Riboflavin	61%
Folate	31%
Vitamin K	141%
Vitamin A	18%
Niacin	17%
Manganese	107%
Potassium	34%
Magnesium	59%
Iron	23%
Calcium	23%
Vitamin E	94%
Fibre	35%

Healthy, Almost Alkaline Pizza Bianchi

An alternative to normal pizza - delicious and much more alkaline!

Serves: 2
Preparation Time: 20 Minutes

Ingredients:
4 sprouted or gluten free wraps
2 cloves of garlic, crushed
6 broccoli florets
2 big handfuls of spinach
1 big handful of rocket
2 tomatoes
Handful of basil leaves
16 black olives
1 green pepper
50ml olive oil
Himalayan salt and black pepper
1/4 fresh lemon
Drizzle of tahini
Optional: sprinkling of parmesan cheese

Instructions:

1. Preheat the oven to 200 degrees or switch on your counter-top pizza oven if you have one!

2. Put the olive oil and garlic into a small mixing bowl and mix to infuse.

3. Lay out the wraps and then spread/brush/drizzle the oil onto the wraps and brush or spread it so that each wrap is entirely covered.

4. Slice the tomatoes and lay these over the 'pizzas' followed by sliced capsicum and put four olives on each.

5. Now chop the broccoli florets in half and spread these evenly over the pizzas too.

6. Drizzle with a little extra olive oil, season and add the parmesan cheese if you're using this.

7. Cook in the oven until the pizzas are starting to just crisp up a little and the toppings are cooked

8. Remove and top with a mix of spinach, rocket and basil

9. Drizzle the tahini, a little more oil and a squeeze of fresh lemon juice and enjoy!

Nutritional Highlights:

This recipe is beneficial for:

Digestion
IBS
Candida
Constipation
Blood Pressure

Each serve contains the following RDA %'s:

Protein	18%
Vitamin A	263%
Vitamin C	252%
Vitamin E	38%
Vitamin K	846%
Riboflavin	17%
Vitamin B6	29%
Folate	77%
Calcium	30%
Iron	38%
Magnesium	31%
Potassium	37%
Sodium	28%
Fiber	39%

Lettuce Tacos

Tasty and Alkaline at the same time - a Definite Must-Try!

Serves: 5-6
Preparation Time: 30 Minutes

Ingredients:
3/4 cups chopped cashew nuts
1 1/2 cups chopped celery
4 to 5 tablespoons sesame garlic sauce or tahini
1 head of lettuce
1/2 pack of firm tofu, diced
1/2 red pepper, diced
Coconut oil
Chopped ginger
Minced onions
Minced garlic

Instructions:

1 Before cooking, chop the celery into small pieces, and crush cashews so that each cashew is broken into about 4 pieces. Perfection not required, just smash 'em up a little.

2 Next, add a little coconut oil and a little water to a frying pan and sprinkle the oil with the freshly minced onions, minced garlic, chooped red pepper, diced tofu and chopped ginger.

3 Pour chopped celery in and steam/fry for about 10 or 15 minutes on medium to high heat.

4 Now add the chopped cashews fry for a further 3 to 4 minutes on low to medium heat. Once it's all looking awesome, remove from heat and mix the sauce/tahini in evenly with celery and cashews.

5 Prepare each serving inside a single large lettuce leaf and enjoy. WARNING: it will get messy, so come to terms with this and make the decision to love it – the messier the better

Nutritional Highlights:

This recipe is beneficial for:

Heart Health
Immune System
Acne
Digestion
PMS

Each serve contains the following RDA %'s:

Protein	4%
Vitamin K	40%
Vitamin B6	7%
Manganese	10%
Magnesium	6%
Iron	3%
Potassium	5%
Vitamin A	25%
Folate	6%
Vitamin C	12%
Dietary Fiber	4%

Gluten-Free Spinach Garlic Tofu Burgers

Everyone's favorite burger patties made healthful, tasty and alkaline!

Serves: 2-4
Preparation Time: 30 Minutes

Ingredients:
16 ounces frozen spinach (organic), thawed
15 ounces firm tofu
3/4 cup gluten free rolled oats
1 medium onion, chopped
3-4 big cloves garlic, minced
1/8 cup nutritional yeast (if transitioning - if not then use LSA mix)
1 tablespoon paprika
salt and pepper to taste
1/4 cup nutritional yeast
1 teaspoon cumin
1/4 cup coconut oil
Optional: dash of Bragg Liquid Amino

Instructions:

1 Crumble tofu, and mix all ingredients together in bowl. Allow to sit a few minutes so oats can absorb some of the liquid from the spinach.

2 Add a little water if your mixture isn't wet enough to hold together. Add the Bragg if desired.

3 Make patties with your hands and fry with a little coconut oil. Cook for 6-10 minutes on each side, turning carefully. Serve with a n

Nutritional Highlights:

This recipe is beneficial for:

Heart Health
Immune System
Acne
Weight Loss
Bloating

Each serve contains the following RDA %'s:

Protein	32%
Vitamin K	755%
Thiamin	32%
Vitamin B6	22%
Magnesium	49%
Iron	37%
Potassium	33%
Vitamin A	235%
Folate	70%
Vitamin C	67%
Riboflavin	16%
Calcium	16%
Vitamin E	13%
Dietary Fiber	28%

Leafy Greens and Ginger Stir-Fry

This delicious stir-fry reflects my love for pumpkins and squashes of all colours and shapes

Serves: 2
Preparation Time: 30 Minutes

Ingredients:
½ a squash, seeds scooped out
and cut into 1cm pieces
1/4 packet of tofu
1 onion, finely sliced
1-2cm piece of ginger, chopped
2-3 garlic cloves, peeled and
chopped
A few handfuls of chopped leafy
greens (kale, spinach, chard etc)
1 red or green chilli, finely chopped
2 tbsp rapeseed oil or sesame oil
Fresh juice of ½ a lemon
Himalayan crystal salt and pepper
A dash of Braggs Liquid Aminos

Instructions:

1 Heat the oil in a large frying pan or a Wok pan and gently fry the onion for a few minutes. Add the ginger, chilli, tofu and garlic. Cook for a minute or so, but be careful that the garlic does not get burnt as it gets bitter otherwise.

2 Add the squash and a pinch of salt. Gently fry until the squash is just tender.

3 Toss in your leafy greens and add in a bit of lemon juice. Add a dash of the Braggs Liquid Aminos and season with pepper to taste.

Nutritional Highlights:

This recipe is beneficial for:

Heart Health
Immune System
Energy
Weight Loss
Bloating

Each serve contains the following RDA %'s:

Protein	16%
Vitamin A	100%
Vitamin C	134%
Vitamin K	315%
Vitamin B6	26%
Folate	34%
Iron	22%
Magnesium	38%
Phosphorus	24%
Potassium	23%
Copper	23%
Manganese	62%
Fibre	24%

Courgette Rolls with Pesto & Red Pepper Dip

Perfect Summer Dish - Great for Entertaining and Sneaking Alkalinity into Your Guests!

Serves: 2
Preparation Time: 20 Minutes

Ingredients:
1 large or 2 small courgettes

For The Pesto Filling
70g pine nuts
3 garlic cloves
1 handful fresh basil and parsley
50ml cold-pressed olive oil
Himalayan salt & black pepper

For The Red Pepper Dip
1 small red pepper
1 garlic clove, cut into fine pieces
3 tsp freshly squeezed lemon juice
Himalayan Crystal Salt and freshly
ground pepper to season

Instructions:

1 Put all ingredients for the pesto filling into a mixer and mix all ingredients on a high setting until you get a creamy consistency.

2 With the help of a peeler "cut" the courgette into long and thin stripes. Put them onto a plate, brush over the pesto, roll together, insert a toothpick to hold the roll together and place them in upright position on a plate.

3 Put all ingredients for the pepper dip into the mixer. Season with salt and pepper.

4 You can either spread the pepper dip over the courgette rolls on the plate or alternatively serve it on a seperate bowl.

Nutritional Highlights:

This recipe is beneficial for:

Heart Health
Immune System
Energy
Weight Loss
Bloating

Each serve contains the following RDA %'s:

Protein	24%
Vitamin C	179%
Vitamin B6	25%
Riboflavin	20%
Folate	22%
Vitamin K	127%
Vitamin A	57%
Thiamin	20%
Niacin	21%
Manganese	321%
Potassium	23%
Magnesium	49%
Iron	25%
Vitamin E	36%
Fibre	23%

Antioxidant Super Soba Salad
This Energizing Meal Keeps You ON THE GO!

Serves: 2
Preparation Time: 10 Minutes

Ingredients:
1/4 Red cabbage thinly sliced
2 Handfuls of spinach leaves
1 yellow pepper
1/2 red onion, diced
4 spring onions, shredded
1/2 cucumber, cut into matchsticks
200g kale, chopped
1/2 broccoli, chopped small
Handful of beansprouts
1 serve of soba noodles
1 handful of coriander leaves
Juice of 1 lime
Bragg Liquid Aminos/Soy Sauce

Optional: handful of alfalfa sprouts
and if transitioning, add 1 kiwi fruit
for extra antioxidants!

Instructions:

1 Firstly, tear the coriander and squeeze the lime juice over it to marinate a little.

2 Now slice everything as indicated above and quickly prepare the soba noodles (they don't take long).

3 Then simply mix everything together in a big salad bowl with the Bragg or soy sauce and eat!

4 With the Bragg or Soy choice it is up to you. If you want to keep this meal as being highly alkaline then go for the Bragg because soy sauce is quite acidifying in the body. You can also add the kiwi fruit if you are just starting out for some sweetness and another antioxidant hit.

Nutritional Highlights:

This recipe is beneficial for:

Heart Health
Immune System
Acne
Weight Loss
Bloating
Anti-Aging

Each serve contains the following RDA %'s:

Protein	32%
Vitamin A	359%
Vitamin C	302%
Vitamin E	14%
Vitamin K	881%
Thiamin	26%
Riboflavin	27%
Vitamin B6	40%
Folate	89%
Calcium	18%
Iron	28%
Magnesium	42%
Potassium	50%
Manganese	100%
Fiber	44%

Chilli Tofu Pitta Breads

A delicious, filling lunch or snack with a kick of chilli and a refreshing Mexican coriander dressing

Serves: 2
Preparation Time: 20 Minutes

Ingredients:
4 pitta breads or wraps
2 cloves of garlic, minced
1 avocado
2 green chillis (or more or less to taste)
8 cherry tomatoes
200g firm tofu
1/2 teaspoon of any Mexican seasoning mix OR
1/4 teaspoon cayenne pepper and
1/4 teaspoon ground coriander
40g cucumber (2 inch slice)
1/2 small red onion
A handful of fresh coriander
1/4 green pepper
Himalayan salt and pepper
Flax oil
1/2 lime, juiced

Instructions:

1   Turn the oven on to 200 degrees and then in a blender or food processor, blend together half of the minced garlic, chillis (add a bit at a time to make sure it isn't to hot for you!), seasonings, half of the coriander and onion.

2   Next, grate the tofu with a grater or the grater blade on your food processor if you have one and add it to the mix, stiring in.

3   Now chop the pitta breads into triangles and spoon the mixture into the pita triangles.

4   Place in the oven for 10 minutes to warm.

5   While this is warming, make the Mexican dressing by blending the cherry tomatoes, remaining garlic, capsicum, cucumber and coriander with a pinch of the salt and pepper and a little drizzle of flax and the lime juice.

6   Remove the pitta pockets from the oven and spoon over the Mexican dressing before finally adding the slices of avocado on top as a garnish.

Nutritional Highlights:

This recipe is beneficial for:

Heart Health
Immune System
Acne
Digestion
PMS

Each serve contains the following RDA %'s:

Protein	50%
Vitamin A	35%
Vitamin C	252%
Vitamin E	13%
Vitamin K	95%
Vitamin B6	40%
Folate	40%
Calcium	20%
Iron	34%
Magnesium	17%
Potassium	24%
Sodium	28%
Fiber	81%

Alkalising Chilli Spring Greens

This is a fabulous and highly alkalising recipe

Serves:
2 as a main dish, 4 as a side dish
Preparation Time: 30 Minutes

Ingredients:
500g spring greens leaves,
finely chopped
2 tbs olive oil
6 tbs yeast-free vegetable stock
1-2 garlic cloves, finely chopped
2 medium onions, thinly sliced
1 fresh red chilli, finely sliced
Juice of 1 fresh lemon
Himalayan crystal salt
Freshly ground black pepper

Optional: Brown basmati rice,
cooked as per instructions

Instructions:

1 Cook the spring greens in the stock or water in a large frying pan over medium heat, covered, for about 5 minutes.

2 In another frying pan, heat the oil over a medium heat and gently fry the onion, garlic and chilli for about 3-4 minutes.

3 Add these to the spring greens, then cover and steam for about 10 minutes. Season to taste with salt and pepper, add the lemon juice and serve.

Nutritional Highlights:

This recipe is beneficial for:

Digestion
Osteoporosis
Kidneys
Liver

Each serve contains the following RDA %'s:

Vitamin C	67%
Vitamin B6	20%
Folate	10%
Manganese	11%
Vitamin K	400%

Alkaline Sushi Recipe

Here are my Alkaline Sushi rolls! With just a few tweaks sushi gets the alkaline makeover

Serves: 4
Preparation Time: 30 Minutes

Ingredients:
215g (1 cup) brown rice
4 nori sheets
1 ripe avocado, peeled, mashed
1/2 cucumber, cut into thin strips
1/2 red capsicum, deseeded, cut into thin strips
1/3 cup coarsely grated carrot
Bragg Liquid Aminos

Optional: fresh red chilli or dried chilli flakes

Optional: firm tofu

Instructions:

1. Cook the brown rice according to the packet instructions and then place in a large bowl. Using a fork, mash in 1/4 of an avocado with the rice to give it that traditional 'sticky' feel of Japanese sushi rice. This way is much more alkaline!

2. Slice all of the vegetables, and if you're using tofu too, quickly fry this in coconut oil and a little Bragg Liquid Aminos (soy sauce replacement)

3. Place a nori sheet, shiny-side down, on a clean surface. Use wet hands to spread one-quarter of the rice mixture over half the nori sheet, leaving a 2cm-wide border along the edge closest to you.

4. Spread about a quarter of the remaining avocado across the centre of the rice. Arrange one-quarter of the capsicum and cucumber across the avocado and top with one-quarter of the grated carrot. If you're using the tofu, place this in here now too.

5. Roll up firmly to enclose filling. Brush edge of nori with warm water to seal. Repeat with remaining nori, rice, avocado, capsicum, cucumber and carrot. Set rolls aside, seam-side down, for 5 minutes to rest.

6. Cut each roll into 6 pieces. Serve with Bragg and optional chilli!

Nutritional Highlights:

This recipe is beneficial for:

Libido
Thyroid
Blood Pressure
Cholesterol
Osteoporosis

Each serve contains the following RDA %'s:

Vitamin B6	16%
Pantothenic Acid	10%
Manganese	35%
Magnesium	10%
Potassium	13%
Vitamin K	25%
Folate	15%
Vitamin C	75%
Vitamin A	72%
Fibre	23%

Dinner

Marinated Salmon Fillet Asian Style

Enjoy this delicious and flavoursome recipe!

Serves: 4
Preparation Time: 30 Minutes

Ingredients:
800g salmon fillet with skin
30g fresh coriander
2 red chillies
1 tbsp black peppercorns
50g fresh ginger
2 lemongrass stalks
Fresh lime peel from 4 organic/
unwaxed limes
2 tbsp Bragg's Liquid Aminos
20g Himalayan Crystal Salt or
Celtic Sea Salt
1 tbsp oyster sauce
1 handful of sesame seeds

Instructions:

1 For the marinade wash the coriander, drain it and hack it into fine pieces. Crush the peppercorns in a mortar, wash the chillies, halve and deseed them and cut into fine pieces.

2 Wash the lemongrass and cut into thin slices. Wash the ginger and cut into small dices.

3 Mix the coriander with the lime peel, ginger, lemongrass, pepper, chilli, salt, oyster and Bragg's Liquid Aminos.

4 Lay the salmon fillet skin side down into a form which the salmon fits in and spread the marinade evenly over the salmon filet. Cover the salmon with cling film and let the marinade soak in for two days in the fridge.

5 Roast the sesame seeds in a frying pan without any fat until they turn golden. Remove the whole marinade from the salmon fillet after two days and sprinkle the sesame seeds onto the salmon.

6 To serve cut the salmon into thin slices.

Nutritional Highlights:

This recipe is beneficial for:

Digestion
IBS
Candida
Constipation
Blood Pressure

Each serve contains the following RDA %'s:

Folate	10%
Iron	23%
Magnesium	10%
Potassium	14%
Manganese	135%
Vitamin A	12%
Vitamin C	32%
Vitamin K	29%

Spelt Pasta with Brocolli and Almonds

A Tasty Alkaline Meal Perfect for Pasta Lovers

Serves: 4
Preparation Time: 30 Minutes

Ingredients:
800g Broccoli
250g Spelt Pasta
150g Almond flakes
2 Garlic cloves, cut into fine pieces
2 tbsp olive oil
Himalayan Crystal Salt or Celtic Sea Salt
Freshly ground black pepper

Instructions:

1   Bring a large pot with water to boil. Cook the pasta until tender, but make sure they are still 'al dente'. Wash and drain the broccoli and cut the florets into small pieces.

2   Gently heat the oil in a large frying pan and add the garlic pieces. Quickly fry them, but make sure they do not become too golden, as they will taste bitter otherwise. Add the broccoli and fry with the garlic.

3   Add a little bit of water and cook until the broccoli becomes tender. Add a little bit more water in the meantime.

4   Meanwhile, roast the almond flakes in a different frying pan at medium heat without adding any oil.

5   As soon as the broccoli is tender stir in the pasta. Mix everything well. Add the almond flakes and season to taste with salt and pepper.

Nutritional Highlights:

This recipe is beneficial for:

Digestion
IBS
Candida
Constipation
Blood Pressure

Each serve contains the following RDA %'s:

Vitamin C	39%
Vitamin K	32%
Manganese	42%
Phosphorous	12%
Magnesium	10%
Fibre	14%

Soba Noodle, Seaweed & Thai Vegetable Salad
A nutritional powerhouse!

Serves: 2
Preparation Time: 15 Minutes

Ingredients:
10g wakame
2 serves of soba noodles
1 cucumber
1 carrot
2 tbsp sesame seeds
2 spring onions
1 inch of fresh ginger
1 garlic clove
1 tbsp sesame oil
1/2 fresh lime, juiced
Bragg liquid aminos

Instructions:

1   Prepare the wakame according to the packet instructions, but roughly it will be to cover in a bowl with cold water for 10 minutes and drain.

2   Prepare the veggies: cut the cucumber and carrot into matchsticks and thinly slice the spring onions. Crush the ginger and garlic in a garlic press.

3   Cook the soba noodles and drain, drizzle with a little sesame oil to keep separate.

4   Finally toss all ingredients together and serve with an extra sprinkle of sesame seeds on top and a splash of Bragg aminos (a soy sauce alternative).

Nutritional Highlights:

This recipe is beneficial for:

Heart Health
Acne
Digestion
IBS
Candida

Each serve contains the following RDA %'s:

Protein	21%
Vitamin K	295%
Vitamin C	56%
Vitamin A	125%
Vitamin B6	18%
Folate	25%
Thiamin	14%
Potassium	21%
Manganese	43%
Magnesium	28%
Copper	37%
Iron	22%
Calcium	23%
Dietary Fiber	30%

Coconut Quinoa and Sweet Potato Curry

This one is a WINNER!

Serves: 4-5
Preparation Time: 30 Minutes

Ingredients:
1 can chickpeas drained
1/2 cup dry quinoa
1 medium-large sweet potato, cubed
1/2 medium onion, chopped
2 to 3 cloves garlic, minced
2 to 3 tablespoons coconut oil
1 teaspoon coriander
1 teaspoon cumin
1 teaspoon turmeric
3/4 teaspoon garlic powder
1/2 teaspoon cayenne
1/8 teaspoon cardamon
1/8 teaspoon ginger
Himalayan salt & black pepper
1 can coconut milk

Instructions:

1 Prepare quinoa, chickpeas, and sweet potatoes. In a saucepan, add chickpeas, quinoa and 300ml of water. Heat over medium-high heat to bring chickpea liquid to a boil. Cover with a tight-fitting lid and reduce heat; simmer for 15 minutes, or until quinoa and chickpeas have softened. Now steam the sweet potato until it is tender (about 15 mins).

2 In a skillet/pan, heat coconut oil over medium heat. Add onion and garlic and saute until the onion is translucent.

3 Add all of the spices (coriander, cumin, turmeric, garlic powder, cayenne pepper, cardamon, ginger, salt, and pepper).

4 Add the chickpea-quinoa-sweet potato mixture to the skillet. Add coconut milk.

5 Mix well and allow to boil over high heat. Reduce to low heat, cover, and simmer for 10 to 15 minutes, stirring every few minutes, until the milk has condensed into a nice curry.

Nutritional Highlights:

This recipe is beneficial for:

Eczema
Blood Pressure
Cholesterol
Bad breath
Weight Loss

Each serve contains the following RDA %'s:

Vitamin B6	19%
Folate	13%
Vitamin C	10%
Manganese	47%
Phosphorous	10%
Magnesium	10%
Vitamin A	84%
Vitamin K	22%
Fibre	17%

Romanesco Cauliflower Curry
An Alkaline Vegetable Curry Rich with Tasty Oriental Flavors

Serves 2 as a main dish
Serves 4 as a side dish
Preparation Time: 40 Minutes

Ingredients:
1 medium sized romanesco
cauliflower, cut into florets
1 or 2 large garlic cloves, chopped
1 red or white onion, chopped
1 tablespoon fresh ginger, sliced
3 handfuls frozen peas, defrosted
1 handful chopped parsley or
fresh coriander
1/2 tablespoon curry powder
1/2 tablespoon garam masala
1 teaspoon grated lemon peel
1 tablespoon olive or rapeseed oil
Himalayan salt
Freshly ground black pepper
1 fresh chilli, cut into fine pieces

Instructions:

1 If served as a side dish cook brown basmati rice as per instructions.

2 Preheat your oven to gas mark 6 or 200 Celsius. Put the onions, garlic, cauliflower, ginger, lemon peel, garam masala, curry powder, oil, chilli, salt and pepper into a large bowl. Mix all ingredients together and make sure that all vegetables are coated with the oil.

3 Spread the mixture onto a large baking tray and roast for about 25 minutes whilst turning regularly.

4 Transfer vegetables into a serving bowl and mix in the peas and fresh parsley or coriander.

Nutritional Highlights:

This recipe is beneficial for:

Immune System
Acne
Digestion
Candida
Colds & Flu

Each serve contains the
following RDA %'s:

Vitamin C	30%
Vitamin B6	18%
Folate	10%
Potassium	12%
Copper	10%
Manganese	22%
Vitamin A	25%
Vitamin K	60%
Fibre	12%

Alkaline Root Vegetable Curry

This healthy meal will have you going crazy over curry!

Serves: 4-6
Preparation Time: 90 Minutes

Ingredients:
7 large handfuls of peeled and diced root vegetables of your choice
3 tbsp olive or coconut oil
3 large garlic cloves, chopped
1 red chilli, roughly chopped
1 large onion, chopped
1 tin of chopped tomatoes
A bunch of fresh coriander
2 cinnamon sticks
3 tsp ground turmeric
2 tsp cumin seeds
1 tsp fennel seeds
2 tsp coriander
1 piece of fresh ginger, sliced thinly
1 tin of coconut milk
1 lime
Himalayan salt and brown pepper

Optional: Brown basmati rice

Instructions:

1 Preheat the oven to 200C. Put one large roasting tray into the oven to heat up.

2 Cut the root vegetables into about 3cm sized dices and put into a bowl. Coat with oil and season with salt and pepper. Put the vegetables onto the tray when it is hot and shake to distribute evenly. Roast them for about 40 mins.

3 Toast the coriander, fennel seeds and cumin in a dry frying pan for a couple of minutes. Grind them to a rough powder and mix in the turmeric.

4 Put the chilli, ginger, garlic and onion in a blender and puree. Gently heat a splash of oil in a frying pan over a medium-low temperature and put in the spices. Fry for about a minute and add the paste. Stir for about 5 mins until the paste has soften and reduced in volume. Add more oil if needed.

5 Stir in the coconut milk and tomatoes. Add the cinnamon, simmer and stir constantly. Season to taste. Pour the sauce over the roasting vegetables.

6 Bake everything for about 25 mins, until the vegetables are tender and the sauce has thickened. Finish with fresh lime juice squeezed over it and garnish with fresh coriander leaves.

Optional: This curry dish is delicious by itself, but please feel free to serve it with brown basmati rice.

Nutritional Highlights:

This recipe is beneficial for:

Weight Loss
Bloating
PMS
Kidney
Bad Breath

Each serve contains the following RDA %'s:

Vitamin A	248%
Vitamin K	32%
Vitamin C	38%
Vitamin B6	15%
Potassium	16%
Manganese	15%
Fibre	14%

Tofu Brazil Nut Steam-Fry

A super tasty dish is this simple yet full of flavour!

Serves: 2
Preparation Time: 30 Minutes

Ingredients:
2 leeks, washed, trimmed and
finely sliced
1 tsp tamari sauce
2 carrots, trimmed, peeled and cut
into fine matchsticks
225g block firm tofu, cut into cubes
100g baby corn, halved lengthways
3 celery stalks, trimmed and sliced
3-4 tbsp chopped brazil nuts
1 tsp sesame oil
1 tsp orange rind
Juice of 1/2 a fresh lime

Instructions:

1 Heat a large wok, add a little water and then the leeks and tamari. Steam fry for a few minutes then add the carrots, tofu and sweetcorn. Cook for a further 5 minutes.

2 Add the celery, brazil nuts, sesame oil and orange rind. Serve immediately on a bed of salad leaves and squeeze over the lime.

3 For extra zing you can add some chilli and if you like a soy-sauce taste I recommend Bragg Liquid Aminos which you can find at Energise.

Nutritional Highlights:

This recipe is beneficial for:

Heart Health
Acne
Digestion
IBS
Candida

Each serve contains the
following RDA %'s:

Protein	35%
Vitamin A	240%
Vitamin C	28%
Vitamin E	12%
Vitamin K	85%
Thiamin	26%
Vitamin B6	24%
Folate	29%
Calcium	32%
Iron	24%
Magnesium	46%
Potassium	24%
Manganese	80%
Fiber	36%

Oriental Vegetable Stew with Chickpeas

This recipe is very popular in Arabic countries due to its abundance of oriental spices.

Serves: 2
Preparation Time: 30 Minutes

Ingredients:
3 large onions
2 medium sized new potatoes
200g chickpeas
1 large or 2 medium sized carrots
1 yellow or red pepper
1 courgette
1 small fresh red chilli
3 tbsp sesame oil
A pinch of black pepper
A pinch of ground cumin
A pinch of ground coriander
A pinch of ground ginger
A pinch of ground cardamom
1 tbsp of himalayan crystal salt

Instructions:

1 Soak the chickpeas in cold water over night. On the next day cook the chickpeas in about double the amount of water for about one hour. In the meantime peel the onions and cut into rings.

2 Wash the potatoes, peel and cut them into ca. 2cm sized pieces. Wash and peel the carrots and cut into ca. 2cm sized pieces. Wash the pepper, remove the stalk and seeds and cut into rings. Wash the courgette and cut into ca. 2cm thick slices.

3 Heat the sesame oil in a large frying pan and add the onions.

4 Deseed the chilli and cut into fine pieces. Add the cumin, pepper, coriander, chilli, ginger, cardamom and salt and gently fry together with the onions.

5 Add the courgette, pepper, potato and carrot pieces and briefly fry. Add a cup of water to deglaze everything. Drain the cooked chickpeas and add to the vegetable stew. Add another cup of water at the end.

Nutritional Highlights:

This recipe is beneficial for:

Digestion
IBS
Candida
Constipation
Blood Pressure

Each serve contains the following RDA %'s:

Protein	29%
Vitamin A	250%
Vitamin C	269%
Vitamin K	28%
Thiamin	18%
Riboflavin	17%
Niacin	17%
Vitamin B6	97%
Folate	50%
Iron	19%
Magnesium	25%
Potassium	55%
Zinc	13%
Manganese	78%
Fiber	69%

Stuffed Tomatoes and Peppers

Highly Nutritious and Enjoyable - Kale Orexe!

Serves: 4
Preparation Time: 80 Minutes

Ingredients:
1 green pepper
1 red or yellow pepper
2 large ripe tomatoes
2 onions, chopped
2 garlic cloves, crushed
50g blanched almonds, chopped
75 g of brown basmati rice, boiled
Handful of mint, roughly chopped
Handful of parsley, roughly chopped
3 tbsp ground almonds
4 tbsp extra virgin olive oil, plus
extra for sprinkling
Chopped mixed herbs, to garnish
Himalayan salt & black pepper

Instructions:

1. Preheat the oven to 190C/Gas 5. Cut the tomatoes in half and scoop out the pulp and seeds with a spoon. Be careful not to damage the skin of the tomatoes whilst doing this. Leave the tomatoes to drain on kitchen paper or a chopping board with cut sides down. Roughly chop the pulp and seeds.

2. Halve the peppers, leaving the cores intact and scoop out the seeds. Brush the peppers with 1 tbsp of olive oil and bake on a baking tray for ca. 15 minutes. Place the peppers and tomatoes in an ovenproof dish and season with salt and pepper. In the meantime boil the rice as per instructions.

3. Gently fry the onions in the remaining oil for about 5 minutes until they start to soften. Add the chopped almonds and garlic and fry for a further minute.

4. Remove the pan from the heat and stir in the boiled rice, chopped tomatoes, parsley and mint. Season well with salt and pepper and fill the tomatoes and peppers with this mixture.

5. Pour 150ml of boiling water around the peppers and tomatoes and bake, uncovered, for about 20 minutes. Scatter with the ground almonds and sprinkle with a little olive oil. Return to the oven and bake for a further 20 minutes until they start to turn golden.

6. Serve garnished with fresh herbs.

Nutritional Highlights:

This recipe is beneficial for:

Anti-Inflammatory
Anti-Aging
Immune System
Heart Health

Each serve contains the following RDA %'s:

Protein	22%
Vitamin A	78%
Vitamin C	300%
Vitamin E	36%
Vitamin K	314%
Riboflavin	13%
Niacin	16%
Vitamin B6	37%
Folate	31%
Iron	15%
Magnesium	26%
Potassium	34%
Copper	21%
Manganese	63%
Fiber	45%

Spicy Aubergine Pasta

A Great Example of an 80% Alkaline and 20% Acid Meal - Very Filling!

Serves: 2
Preparation Time: 30 Minutes

Ingredients:
200g spelt or vegetable pasta
1 large aubergine (eggplant)
1 red pepper (capsicum)
3 tomatoes
A handful of baby spinach
1 medium-sized red onion
2 cloves of garlic
1 small chilli
150ml yeast-free vegetable stock
1 handful of fresh basil
1/2 teaspoon Himalayan salt
1 pinch of cayenne pepper
Drizzle of cold-pressed olive oil
1 teaspoon of coconut oil

Instructions:

1 Firstly get the pasta on, spelt pasta takes a little longer than normal pasta.

2 Now get the veggies going. Start by chopping the aubergine and tomatoes into medium sized chunks (a little bigger than a cubed cm), slicing the pepper, onion, chilli and dicing the garlic. Tear the basil up.

3 Now warm the coconut oil in a pan and lightly cook the onion and garlic, then throw in the aubergine. Once the aubergine has browned a bit, chuck in the tomato, capsicum and then add the stock, salt and cayenne pepper. Let this simmer for ten minutes until it is starting to reduce a bit and get a bit saucy.

4 Once the pasta is cooked, you're almost there. For the final 30 seconds just throw in the basil and spinach to just let it wilt slightly. Now serve over the pasta and drizzle very lightly with the olive oil.

Optional: If you're transitioning, you can add olives or a sprinkling of parmesan

Nutritional Highlights:

This recipe is beneficial for:

Heart Health
Immune System
Acne
Digestion
PMS

Each serve contains the following RDA %'s:

Protein	17%
Vitamin A	181%
Vitamin C	271%
Vitamin E	14%
Vitamin K	400%
Riboflavin	15%
Niacin	16%
Vitamin B6	50%
Folate	59%
Calcium	10%
Iron	14%
Magnesium	24%
Potassium	46%
Manganese	94%
Fiber	63%

Soba Pasta Pesto Pine Extravaganza!

Combined with fresh, raw pesto, uncooked oil and pine nuts, this meal is a great transition recipe.

Serves: 2
Preparation Time: 30 Minutes

Ingredients:
1 pack of soba noodles
(depending on pack size, make
the noodles just 20% of your
plate)
250g pine nuts (pref organic)
1 cup of cold-pressed olive oil,
flax oil or Udo's Choice
1 bunch of basil, plus parsley and
coriander to taste
Himalayan Crystal Salt
Freshly ground pepper

Optional: extra veggies, steamed
such as zucchini, broccoli, tomato
(raw), rocket, peas, etc, or serve
with a big side salad of rocket.

Instructions:

1 Cook the soba noodles as per instructions on the packet.
Remember to keep the noodles to 20% of the plate.

2 Give the herbs a good wash (basil, coriander and parsley) and
blend these up with the pine nuts and a tiny amount of oil to get it
going. Once these are blended, toss in the rest of the ingredients
and blend
until you get a creamy sauce.

3 At this stage if you're going to have with other veggies or a salad,
prepare this now.

4 Once the veggies are ready and the noodles are cooked, I like
to toss together with the pesto in a saucepan to warm gently.
Season with salt and pepper and you're ready to go!

Nutritional Highlights:

This recipe is beneficial for:

Kidneys
Liver
Energy
Weight Loss
Bloating

Each serve contains the
following RDA %'s:

Protein	43%
Vitamin A	58%
Vitamin C	42%
Vitamin E	60%
Vitamin K	498%
Thiamin	34%
Riboflavin	17%
Niacin	28%
Folate	20%
Iron	45%
Magnesium	81%
Potassium	25%
Zinc	54%
Manganese	571%
Fiber	23%

Salmon Steak with Broccolini

This delicious recipe contains an oily fish which is rich in the healthy essential fatty acids

Serves: 2
Preparation Time: 30 Minutes

Ingredients:
2 x Salmon steaks (about 200g each)
2 tbsp extra virgin olive oil
2 tbsp olive oil
500g broccolini
Handful of fresh parsley
Handful of fresh chives
2 slices of lemon
Juice of 1 lemon
Himalayan Crystal Salt or celtic sea salt
Freshly ground black pepper

Instructions:

1 Mix together the lemon juice and olive oil. Marinate the salmon steaks in there for about 20 minutes. In the meantime wash and drain the broccolini and cut into florets.

2 Heat the olive oil in a frying pan and fry the salmon at low heat on each side for about 5-8 minutes. Pour the rest of the marinade over the fish and steam for a few minutes. Season with salt and pepper.

3 In the meantime steam the broccoli florets until they are al dente.

4 Arrange the salmon and broccoli on a plate. Pour the remaining sauce from the frying pan over the fish and garnish with chives, parsley and slices of lemon.

Nutritional Highlights:

This recipe is beneficial for:

**Heart Health
Blood Pressure
Cholesterol
Liver
Brain Health
Muscle Development**

Each serve contains the following RDA %'s:

Protein	119%
Vitamin A	66%
Vitamin C	441%
Vitamin E	15%
Vitamin K	657%
Thiamin	49%
Riboflavin	76%
Niacin	100%
Vitamin B6	117%
Folate	63%
Calcium	15%
Iron	28%
Magnesium	31%
Potassium	61%
Fiber	29%

Chinese Stir Fry Buckwheat Noodles

This Healthy Meal by Energise Fan Eliza Miesch is Sure to Fill You Up!

Serves: 2
Preparation Time: 60 Minutes

100g buckwheat flour
50-60 ml water
1 tbsp olive oil
¼ tsp sea salt
1 carrot
1 bulb of bok choi
1/2 chinese cabbage
1/4 red cabbage
1 fennel bulb
1 red pepper
5 spring onions
2 cloves garlic
1 tbsp olive or flaxseed oil
1 tbsp Bragg Liquid Aminos
Salt and pepper

Instructions:

1 Firstly, prepare the noodles by placing the buckwheat flour in a bowl and making a well in the centre. Add the rest of the ingredients (with 50ml water) in the centre and slowly mix in the flour. Then knead till a pliable dough is formed. If too dry add another 5 ml water. Wrap in cling film and put in the fridge for ½ hour.

2 Meanwhile wash and prepare vegetables, except for the bean sprouts.

3 Place dough on a lightly dusted (with buckwheat flour) worktop. Roll it out to roughly 1mm thick evenly. It doesn't matter in what shape the dough is. T hen cut into thin long stripes.

4 Get a small pot of water boiling. Fill another bowl with cold tap water and place in the sink. When water boils turn heat down to medium and put all the noodles in. The noodles are cooked when they float to the surface. Use a slotted spoon or sieve to dish them out and put them straight into the bowl with cold water and keep running cold water in the bowl to cool the noodles.

5 While the noodles are cooling down, heat a frying pan with olive oil and sauté onions and garlic for ½ min. Add carrot and stir-fry for another ½ min. Add the rest of the vegetables and keep stir-frying for ½ min. Drain the noodles and add to the vegetables.

6 Add soya sauce, salt and pepper to taste.

Nutritional Highlights:

This recipe is beneficial for:

Heart Health
Blood Pressure
Cholesterol
Osteoporosis
Liver

Each serve contains the following RDA %'s:

Protein	22%
Vitamin A	201%
Vitamin C	275%
Vitamin K	213%
Vitamin B6	50%
Folate	45%
Magnesium	38%
Potassium	29%
Manganese	79%
Fiber	45%

Aubergine Stew with Spicy Chick-Peas

Flavoursome Stew that Will Get Your Tastebuds Tingling with Delight!

Serves: 4
Preparation Time: 90 Minutes

Ingredients:
200g chick peas, soaked overnight
3 large aubergines, cut into cubes
3 onions, chopped
2 garlic cloves, chopped
4 tbsp olive oil
3 x 400g cans of chopped tomatoes
1/2 tsp ground cumin
1/2 tsp ground coriander
1/2 tsp ground cinnamon
Himalayan salt & black pepper
Brown basmati rice

For The Garnish:
1 onion, finely sliced
1 garlic clove, sliced
2 tbsp olive oil
Sprigs of fresh coriander

Instructions:

1 Cut the aubergines into cubes, place them in a colander and sprinkle them with salt. Leave the colander sitting in a bowl and leave for about 20 minutes, so that the bitter juices can escape. Rinse with cold water and let them drain.

2 Drain the chick peas, put them in a pan with enough water to cover and bring to the boil. Simmer for about 30 minutes, or until they are tender. Drain.

3 Heat the oil in a large pan. Add the onion and garlic and cook gently, until they have started to soften. Add all the spices and cook whilst stirring. After a few seconds add the aubergine and stir so that the cubes get coated with the onion and spices. Cook for about 5 minutes.

4 Add the chick peas and tomatoes and season to taste with salt and pepper. Cover the saucepan and simmer for about 20-25 minutes.

5 For the garnish: Heat the oil in a frying pan, add the garlic and onion and gently fry until golden.

Tip: For a nice presentation fill the bowls with the rice, then add the stew and top everything with the garlic, onion and coriander sprigs.

Nutritional Highlights:

This recipe is beneficial for:

Kidneys
Liver
Energy
Weight Loss
Bloating

Each serve contains the following RDA %'s:

Protein	18%
Vitamin A	10%
Vitamin C	37%
Vitamin K	61%
Thiamin	15%
Niacin	17%
Vitamin B6	41%
Folate	37%
Iron	10%
Magnesium	23%
Potassium	29%
Copper	23%
Manganese	104%
Fiber	73%

Chickpea Korma with Brown Rice

Another delicious alkaline recipe for you all to try!

Serves: 2
Preparation Time: 50 Minutes

Ingredients:
1 tbsp coconut oil
1 large onion, finely chopped
1 garlic clove, finely chopped
1 tsp curry powder
1 tsp ground cumin
1 tsp ground coriander
1 tsp turmeric
1 tsp sesame seeds
2 tsp ginger
1 tsp garam masala
50g coconut cream
1 tin of chickpeas
2 carrots, sliced
1 medium sweet potato
half a cauliflower, cut into florets
1 tbsp arrowroot dissolved in 1 tbsp water
1 tbsp chopped coriander
2 cups of brown rice

Instructions:

1 Rinse the rice and put in a pan with twice the amount of water. Bring to the boil, turn down the heat and simmer with the lid on until all the water is absorbed (about 40 minutes).

2 Heat the coconut oil in a large saucepan and add the onion and garlic. Cook them until they soften. Add the spices, except the garam masala, and cook for a few more minutes.

3 Add the carrots, sweet potato and cauliflower and cook for a few minutes, coating them in the spices. Dissolve the creamed coconut in 2 cups of boiling water and add it to the pan with the drained and rinsed chickpeas. Cook for 10 minutes until the vegetables are cooked through.

4 Add the arrowroot mixture and cook until the mixture thickens. Add the fresh coriander and sesame seeds just before serving.

Nutritional Highlights:

This recipe is beneficial for:

Heart Health
Immune System
Energy
Weight Loss
Bloating

Each serve contains the following RDA %'s:

Protein	33%
Vitamin A	442%
Vitamin C	149%
Vitamin K	41%
Riboflavin	10%
Niacin	19%
Vitamin B6	74%
Folate	43%
Iron	26%
Magnesium	39%
Potassium	30%
Sodium	17%
Fiber	70%

Broccoli and Potato Curry

Coconut milk adds an extra kick of flavor to this alkaline dish

Serves: 4
Preparation Time: 30 Minutes

Ingredients:
500g broccoli
800g potatoes (preferably red potatoes)
2 small onions or 1 large onion
1 can of coconut milk (preferably organic)
400ml yeast-free vegetable stock
2 tbsp coconut oil or rapeseed oil
100g red lentils
1 1/2 tbsp red curry paste
Himalayan crystal salt or celtic sea salt
Freshly ground black pepper

Instructions:

1   Peel the potatoes and cut into cube sized pieces. Wash the broccoli and cut into florets. Peel the onion(s) and cut into fine pieces.

2   Heat the oil in a large pan and gently fry the onion and potatoes for a few minutes. Add the coconut milk, vegetable stock and curry paste. Cover with a lid and gently cook on medium heat for about 10 minutes.

3   Add the lentils and broccoli and cook for a further 10 minutes.

4   Season curry with salt and pepper.

Nutritional Highlights:

This recipe is beneficial for:

Heart Health
Blood Pressure
Cholesterol
Osteoporosis
Liver

Each serve contains the following RDA %'s:

Protein	66%
Vitamin A	30%
Vitamin C	523%
Vitamin K	331%
Thiamin	64%
Riboflavin	32%
Vitamin B6	104%
Folate	126%
Calcium	18%
Iron	60%
Magnesium	63%
Potassium	100%
Manganese	149%
Selenium	27%
Fiber	138%

Alkaline Lentil Ratatouille
An Interesting Twist to The Classic Ratatouille

Serves: 2
Preparation Time: 30 Minutes

Ingredients:
2 red peppers, cut into cube size pieces
1 leek, cut into fine rings
1 small tin of lentils
1 tin of organic chopped tomatoes
1 mug of brown basmati rice
1 mug of water
2 tbsp olive oil
1 handful of rosemary, chopped into fine pieces
1 pinch of ground ginger
1 pinch cinnamon
Himalayan Crystal Salt or Celtic Sea Salt
Freshly ground black pepper

Instructions:

1 Cook the rice as per instructions. Gently fry the peppers and leeks in olive oil. Add the chopped tomatoes and simmer for about five minutes.

2 Add the lentils and let everything simmer for about five to ten minutes. Season with salt and pepper and add the rosemary, cinnamon and ginger.

Nutritional Highlights:

This recipe is beneficial for:

Heart Health
Immune System
Acne
Digestion
PMS

Each serve contains the following RDA %'s:

Protein	37%
Vitamin A	120%
Vitamin C	305%
Vitamin E	11%
Vitamin K	54%
Thiamin	42%
Riboflavin	12%
Niacin	25%
Vitamin B6	51%
Folate	89%
Iron	29%
Magnesium	33%
Potassium	37%
Manganese	115%
Fiber	85%

Autumn Pumpkin Stew

This nutritious and alkaline stew will definitely keep you warm and fill you up nicely in these chilly autumn nights!

Serves: 4
Preparation Time: 30 Minutes

Ingredients:
1 kg of pumpkins
1 large or 2 medium sized onions
4 carrots
4 new potatoes
1-2 red chillies
2-3 garlic cloves
1 mug of brown basmati rice
4 tbsp extra native olive oil
1 1/4 litres of yeast-free vegetable stock
A handful of parsley, finely chopped
A pinch of celtic sea salt or himalayan crystal salt
Freshly ground pepper

Instructions:

1 Peel the pumpkin, carrots, onions, garlic cloves and potatoes. Cut the onion into fine pieces and finely chop the garlic cloves. Cut the carrots into slices and cut the potatoes into cubes. Deseed the pumpkin and cut into cubes. Deseed the chillies and cut into fine pieces.

2 Gently fry the onions and garlic in olive oil. Add the rice, mix well, and add pumpkins, carrots, potatoes and the chillies. Steam for about 10 minutes. Add the stock, season with salt and pepper and cook on low heat for another 30 minutes. Stir in the parsley and leave to rest in the open pot for about 5 minutes.

Nutritional Highlights:

This recipe is beneficial for:

IBS
Candida
Eczema
Colds & Flu

Each serve contains the following RDA %'s:

Protein	17%
Vitamin A	468%
Vitamin C	147%
Vitamin E	20%
Vitamin K	171%
Thiamin	14%
Riboflavin	17%
Niacin	14%
Vitamin B6	47%
Folate	14%
Iron	13%
Magnesium	17%
Potassium	55%
Manganese	63%
Fiber	45%

Garlic Tofu with Vietnamese Coleslaw with Lime Dressing

Fresh, refreshing, packed with colour, flavour and alkalinity

Serves: 2
Preparation Time: 25 Minutes

Ingredients:
150g firm tofu
1 carrot
75g finely shredded green cabbage
75g finely shredded red cabbage
1 red pepper, thinly sliced
60g beansprouts or any other sprout
4 spring onions, thinly sliced
1/2 bunch of fresh coriander, chopped
3 cloves of garlic
2cm of fresh ginger
2 limes
Himalayan salt & black pepper
Sesame, olive or coconut oil
Sesame seeds

Instructions:

1 Start by preparing the tofu. Slice the tofu into cubes about 1.5 cm squared.

2 Now crush 2 cloves of the garlic and half of the ginger into a medium bowl and drizzle in some oil until it makes a paste.

3 Now toss in the tofu and mix until the tofu is well covered.

4 Gently heat the oil in a pan and pan fry the ginger and garlic covered tofu until golden. Remove from the heat.

5 Using a vegetable peeler, slice the carrot into ribbons and put in a medium sized bowl with the shredded cabbages, pepper, beansprouts, onion and 3/4 of the coriander and stir and toss.

6 Now combine the juice from the limes, the remaining garlic clove (crushed) and remaining coriander and mix well.

7 Serve by layering the slaw, then the tofu and then drizzle with the lime dressing. Finish with a sprinkling of sesame seeds.

Nutritional Highlights:

This recipe is beneficial for:

Heart Health
Libido
Thyroid
Colds & Flu
Constipation

Each serve contains the following RDA %'s:

Protein	15%
Vitamin A	135%
Vitamin C	188%
Vitamin K	235%
Folate	18%
Calcium	17%
Iron	16%
Magnesium	21%
Potassium	20%
Manganese	44%
Vitamin B6	28%
Copper	34%
Fibre	39%

Red Lentils with Peppers

This dish makes a great main course or accompaniment with healthy fish like salmon.

Serves:
Serves 2 as a main course
Serves 4 as an accompaniment
Preparation Time: 30 Minutes

Ingredients:
2 onions
2 garlic cloves
350g red or yellow peppers
2 tbsp olive oil
250g dried red lentils (precooked according to pack instructions)
1 tsp dried thyme
400ml vegetable stock
4 spring onions
sea salt or himalayan crystal salt
fresh grounded pepper
1-1 1/2 tbsp fresh lemon juice

Instructions:

1 Remove the skin of the onions and cut them into small pieces. Peel the garlic cloves and cut it into slices. Halve the peppers, remove the seeds, wash the pepper halves and cut into slices.

2 Heat the olive oil in a pot. Gently fry the onions and garlic slices. Add the lentils, peppers, thyme and vegetable stock. Bring everything to the boil and cook everything at low heat for about 8 minutes with the lid on.

3 Remove the root ends and the dark green bits of the spring onions, wash them and cut them into rings. Add them to the dish and cook for a further 3 mins with the lid on.

4 Season with salt, pepper and fresh lemon juice to your taste.

Nutritional Highlights:

This recipe is beneficial for:

Heart Health
Immune System
Acne
Digestion
PMS
Muscle Development

Each serve contains the following RDA %'s:

Protein	72%
Vitamin A	109%
Vitamin C	411%
Vitamin E	13%
Vitamin K	111%
Thiamin	78%
Riboflavin	24%
Niacin	25%
Vitamin B6	68%
Folate	155%
Magnesium	45%
Potassium	49%
Manganese	21%
Fiber	179%

Okra with Coriander and Tomatoes

This is a wonderful recipe which contains three of my favourite ingredients

Serves: 4
Preparation Time: 30 Minutes

Ingredients:
450g ripe tomatoes (if there are no ripe tomatoes available you can replace them with a 400g can of chopped tomatoes)
450g fresh okra
3 tbsp olive oil
2 onions, thinly sliced
2 tsp coriander seeds, crushed
3 garlic cloves, crushed
Finely grated rind and juice of 1 organic lemon
Himalayan or celtic sea salt and ground black pepper

Instructions:

1   If using fresh tomatoes, plunge them into boiling water for about 30 seconds, then put under cold water. Peel away the skins and chop the tomatoes.

2   Trim off any stalks from the okra and leave whole. Heat the oil in a deeper frying pan and gently fry the onions and coriander for about 3-4 minutes until the onions begin to soften.

3   Add the okra and garlic and fry for 1 minute. Gently stir in the tomatoes and simmer gently for about 20 minutes, until the okra is tender. Stir occassionally.

4   Stir in the lemon rind and juice and add salt and pepper to taste.

Serve warm or cold.

Nutritional Highlights:

This recipe is beneficial for:

IBS
Candida
Eczema
Colds & Flu
Constipation

Each serve contains the following RDA %'s:

Vitamin A	26%
Vitamin C	73%
Vitamin K	93%
Thiamin	15%
Vitamin B6	18%
Folate	29%
Magnesium	16%
Potassium	17%
Manganese	65%
Fiber	20%

Chickpea Kale Rolls with Tomato Salsa

Not only tastes good - it looks good, too! Perfect for dinner with friends and family.

Serves: 4
Preparation Time: 30 Minutes

Ingredients:

Chickpea Kale Rolls
1 medium sized onion, finely chopped
12 large kale leaves
1 cup cooked chickpeas
1 tsp extra virgin olive oil
3/4 cup yeast-free vegetable stock
1/2 cup brown basmati rice
1/2 tsp ground paprika
1 tsp ground cumin
Pinch of Himalayan Salt

Tomato Salsa
1 onion
1 large can of plum tomatoes
3 jalapeno peppers
1 bunch of coriander

Instructions:

1   Heat the oil in a saucepan over medium heat. Add the onion and gently cook for about 4 minutes, until softened. Add the rice, chickpeas, stock, paprika, cumin and salt. Bring to the boil. Cover with a lid, reduce the heat and let everything simmer for 15 minutes, until the liquid is absorbed. Let it cool.

2   Wash and drain the kale leaves. Trim the thick stems from the center of the leaves. Place 2 small or 1 large leaf overlapping on your kitchen surface. Pull together the cut edges where the stem was removed to overlap.

3   Spoon about 2 tbs of the chickpea and rice mixture in the center of the bottom of the leaf. Fold in the sides and roll up leaf to tip. Repeat the same procedure for the remaining leaves and filling.

4   For making the salsa, use a blender or hand mixer. Pour the plum tomatoes into the blender. Peel the onion and cut into quarters. Place the onions on top of the tomatoes inside the blender. Wash and dry the coriander and cut off the stems. Put the coriander inside the blender. Wash and dry the jalapeno peppers and cut off the stems. Put them into the blender. You can use more or less jalapenos depending on how spicy you like your salsa to be. Blend for 40 seconds or until all ingredients are blended. Be careful not to over blend, as the salsa will thicken otherwise.

5   Serve the Chickpea Kale Rolls on a plate topped wth the Tomato Salsa.

Nutritional Highlights:

This recipe is beneficial for:

Heart Health
Digestion
Eczema
Blood Pressure
Cholesterol

Each serve contains the following RDA %'s:

Protein	13%
Vitamin A	118%
Vitamin C	110%
Vitamin K	302%
Thiamin	51%
Vitamin B6	26%
Folate	15%
Potassium	20%
Copper	10%
Manganese	12%
Fiber	30%

Sides

Broccoli, Carrots and Peas in Coconut Curry Sauce

We hope you enjoy this tasty curry as much as we do and feel free to mix it up with other vegetables!

Serves: 24
Preparation Time: 30 Minutes

Ingredients:
500g broccoli
400g carrots
200g peas, fresh or frozen
2 medium sized onions
3 garlic cloves
200ml coconut milk (unsweetened)
200ml yeast-free vegetable stock
1 lemon (unwaxed)
2 tbsp coconut oil
2 tsp curry powder
Optional: Himalayan crystal salt or celtic sea salt
Freshly ground black pepper

Instructions:

1 Peel the onions and cut into small pieces. Peel the garlic cloves and hack into fine pieces. Wash and drain the broccoli and carrots. Separate the broccoli florets from the stem and cut the carrots into thin slices.

2 Heat 2 tbs of oil in a large frying pan. Gently fry the onion, garlic and curry powder and shortly roast.

3 Add the broccoli and carrots, season with a little bit of salt and briefly fry. Pour in the coconut milk and stock, season with 1/2 tsp grated lemon peel and cover the pan with a lid. Gently cook for about 12 minutes.

4 Season the curry with salt, pepper, 1 tbsp lemon juice and curry powder. Quickly bring back to boil and then serve.

Nutritional Highlights:

This recipe is beneficial for:

Heart Health
Digestion
Eczema
Blood Pressure
Cholesterol

Each serve contains the following RDA %'s:

Protein	44%
Vitamin A	744%
Vitamin C	436%
Vitamin E	10%
Vitamin K	359%
Thiamin	27%
Riboflavin	21%
Vitamin B6	51%
Folate	66%
Calcium	15%
Iron	28%
Magnesium	33%
Potassium	68%
Manganese	125%
Fiber	103%

Fennel with Brown Basmati Rice

Simple but delicious dish for summer

Serves: 2
Preparation Time: 30 Minutes

Ingredients:
6 large fennel bulbs
1 large onion
2 garlic cloves
A few sprigs of dill
Yeast-free vegetable stock
2 tbsp olive oil
Himalayan crystal salt or celtic
sea salt
Freshly ground black pepper
Brown basmati rice, cooked per
instructions

Instructions:

1 Wash and drain the fennel bulbs. Cut off the stalks, cut the bulbs in half and cut out the hard stalks. Cut the bulbs into quarters. Peel the onions and garlic and chop into fine pieces.

2 In the meantime cook the basmati rice as per instructions.

3 Gently heat the olive oil in a large frying pan and gently fry the onions until they start to soften. Add the fennel pieces and garlic and gently fry for about 2-3 minutes. Add hot yeast-free vegetable stock to the pan until the vegetables are slightly covered. Cover the pan with a lid, turn down the heat to the lowest setting and let everything cook for about 20 minutes until the fennel is tender, but not overcooked.

4 Wash and dry the dill and tear. Season with salt and pepper and sprinkle the dill over the vegetables.

5 Serve the vegetables on top of the rice.

Nutritional Highlights:

This recipe is beneficial for:

**PMS
Kidney
Liver
Energy
Osteoporosis**

Each serve contains the following RDA %'s:

Protein	22%
Vitamin C	188%
Folate	63%
Niacin	21%
Vitamin A	42%
Vitamin B6	29%
Riboflavin	12%
Potassium	90%
Manganese	77%
Calcium	37%
Magnesium	34%
Iron	35%
Sodium	15%
Vitamin K	287%
Dietary Fiber	94%

Grilled Aubergine with Salsa Fresca

Super-simple, but flavour-packed lunch that's full of life-giving colour and goodness

Serves: 2
Preparation Time: 20 Minutes

Ingredients:
1 large aubergine or 6 baby
aubergines
3/4 green pepper
3/4 yellow pepper
2 tomatoes
Handful of basil
Handful of coriander
1/2 lemon, juiced
1/2 tbsp coconut or olive oil

Instructions:

1 Start by slicing the aubergine lengthways.

2 Press down firmly on the aubergine each side with a kitchen towel to absorb some of the moisture.

3 Next, heat the oil very lightly on a grill pan (or you can cook under the grill or on a barbecue) until tender.

4 Now finely chop the pepper, tomatoes, basil and coriander and place in a bowl and stir in the lemon juice and an extra drizzle of the olive oil.

5 Simply serve the salsa atop the aubergine and enjoy!

Nutritional Highlights:

This recipe is beneficial for:

Acne
Digestion
Chronic Fatigue
Bad breath
Weight Loss

Each serve contains the following RDA %'s:

Protein	38%
Vitamin C	74%
Vitamin B6	29%
Riboflavin	61%
Folate	31%
Vitamin K	141%
Vitamin A	18%
Niacin	17%
Manganese	107%
Potassium	34%
Magnesium	59%
Iron	23%
Calcium	23%
Vitamin E	94%
Fibre	50%

Vegetable Dhal with Ginger Raita

Filling, quick and very very alkaline - serve as a side or main

Serves: 2
Preparation Time: 30 Minutes

Ingredients:
3cm piece of fresh ginger
2 cloves of garlic
200g yellow split peas or lentils
2 carrots
1 litre of water
1 courgette
Big pinch of turmeric
2 tablespoons of fresh coriander
1 tablespoon of dill
1/4 lime, juiced
1 tablespoon of mint
4 tablespoons of plain soya yoghurt
or coconut 'yoghurt'
Coconut oil or oil of your choice

Instructions:

1 Lightly fry 2cm of the ginger, crushed in a garlic press, the turmeric and the garlic on a very, very low heat until you can smell those delicious fragrances (about 2 minutes).

2 Add the split peas/lentils (that are either pre-prepared from dried or tinned), the carrot, chopped, and water and bring to a boil.

3 Reduce the heat and simmer, covered, for around 20 minutes.

4 While this is simmering, dice the courgette and then after the 20 minutes is up, add this to the pot and cook for a further 3-4 minutes. Once off the heat, stir through half of the coriander, roughly chopped and top with dill.

5 To make the raita, simply chop the mint finely, grate the remaining ginger and mix with the yoghurt/coconut yoghurt and then chill for as long as you can!

Nutritional Highlights:

This recipe is beneficial for:

Heart Health
Digestion
Eczema
Blood Pressure
Cholesterol
Muscle Development

Each serve contains the following RDA %'s:

Protein	59%
Vitamin A	227%
Vitamin C	75%
Vitamin K	76%
Thiamin	61%
Riboflavin	20%
Niacin	16%
Vitamin B6	45%
Folate	129%
Calcium	12%
Iron	44%
Magnesium	35%
Potassium	43%
Manganese	87%
Fiber	137%

Creamy Brussels Sprouts

Creamy, Alkaline and Delicious!

Serves: 2
Preparation Time: 20 Minutes

Ingredients:
10-20 brussels sprouts, halved
2 tablespoons coconut oil
2-4 tablespoons tahini
2-4 teaspoons Bragg (or tamari)
2-4 tablespoons toasted sesame
seeds

Instructions:

1 Steam the Brussels for about 8-10 minutes until they're just
softening, but not going mushy or losing their colour.

2 Drain water off, add oil and place into a pan and saute until
golden brown. Meanwhile, in a bowl, mix tahini and Bragg (or
tamari). If mixture gets really thick, add a little water.

3 Once sprouts are done sauteing, pull off heat and add the tahini/
tamari mixture and mix until all sprouts are coated. This should
not be anything near 'soupy'. If it's a bit watery, get it back on the
heat until it reduces and thickens up.

4 Once all sprouts are coated, pour onto plate/bowl and generously
sprinkle with the sesame seeds.

Nutritional Highlights:

This recipe is beneficial for:

Immune System
Candida
Eczema
Blood Pressure
Cholesterol

Each serve contains the
following RDA %'s:

Protein	22%
Vitamin C	220%
Vitamin K	370%
Thiamin	26%
Riboflavin	10%
Calcium	12%
Phosphorous	22%
Zinc	10%
Copper	24%
Manganese	22%
Sodium	28%
Fiber	32%

Spinach with Almonds

An Alkaline Supermeal - Definite Must-Try!

Serves: 2
Preparation Time: 30 Minutes

Ingredients:
600g fresh spinach
1 small onion
1 garlic clove
1 ripe tomato
8 tbsp oil e.g. flax or coconut oil
80g almonds
1 dried red chilli
1 tsp curry powder
1/2 tsp ground coriander
A pinch of Celtic sea salt or Himalayan salt

Instructions:

1 Wash the spinach and tear into single leaves. Peel the onion and garlic and cut into small pieces. Wash the tomato, cut into dices and take out the stem.

2 Heat a Wok pan or a deep frying pan and heat the oil in it. Roast the almonds and the crumbled chilli whilst stirring until the almonds have turned golden brown. Remove them from the pan and put them onto a sheet of kitchen roll which can soak up the excess oil.

3 Gently fry the onion and garlic until they start to soften. Add the tomato, curry powder and coriander and gently stir-fry for approx. 2 minutes.

4 Add the spinach and stir-fry for a further 2-3 minutes.

5 Season the dish with salt and stir in the roasted almonds. It is optional to add in the chilli crumbles if you like to give it a spicier taste.

Nutritional Highlights:

This recipe is beneficial for:

Kidneys
Liver
Energy
Weight Loss
Bloating

Each serve contains the following RDA %'s:

Protein	37%
Vitamin A	579%
Vitamin C	218%
Vitamin E	130%
Vitamin K	1822%
Thiamin	21%
Riboflavin	57%
Vitamin B6	47%
Folate	157%
Calcium	41%
Iron	53%
Magnesium	87%
Potassium	65%
Fiber	55%

Spinach and Chickpeas
A light snack featuring the most alkaline vegetable - Spinach!

Serves: 4
Preparation Time: 20 Minutes

Ingredients:
2 tbsp extra virgin olive oil
1 big garlic clove, halved
1 onion, peeled and cut into small pieces
1/2 tsp cumin
1 pinch of cayenne pepper
1 pinch of curcuma
800g tinned or fresh chickpeas, cleaned and drained and cooked
Himalayan salt & pepper

Optional: 2 pimientos del piquillo peppers, drained and cut into strips

Instructions:

1 Gently heat the oil in a large frying pan. Add the garlic and fry for about 2 minutes until the garlic halves turn slightly golden without letting them get burnt. Remove the garlic from the pan and discard of it.

2 Add the onion, cumin, cayenne pepper and curcuma and gently fry for about 5 minutes until soft. Add the chickpeas and stir until they have slightly absorbed the colour of the curcuma and cayenne pepper.

3 Stir in the spinach leaves. Put a lid on the pan and gently let it cook for about 4-5 minutes. Add the pimientos del piquillo peppers and cook them whilst carefully stirring wihout the lid, until the moisture has evaporated.

4 Season the dish and serve immediately.

Nutritional Highlights:

This recipe is beneficial for:

Acne
Digestion
Chronic Fatigue
Bad breath
Weight Loss

Each serve contains the following RDA %'s:

Protein	29%
Vitamin A	470%
Vitamin C	152%
Vitamin E	25%
Vitamin K	1510%
Riboflavin	28%
Vitamin B6	126%
Folate	191%
Calcium	38%
Iron	67%
Magnesium	78%
Potassium	43%
Sodium	50%
Manganese	239%
Fiber	96%

Spiced Turnips with Spinach and Tomatoes

A delicious vegetable snack or side dish from the Eastern Mediterranean

Serves 6 as a side dish
Preparation Time: 20 Minutes

Ingredients:
450g plum or other ripe tomatoes
2 onions, sliced
4 tbsp olive oil
450g baby turnips, peeled
1 tsp paprika
4 tbsp chopped fresh coriander
450g fresh young spinach
Himalayan Crystal Salt or Celtic
Sea Salt and freshly ground pepper

Instructions:

1   Plunge the tomatoes into a bowl of boiling water for ca. 30
seconds, then refresh in a bowl of cold water. Peel away the
tomato skins and chop roughly. Heat the olive oil in a large frying
pan and gently fry the onion slices for approx. 5 minutes until
they start to soften and turn golden.

2   Add the baby turnips, tomatoes and paprika to the pan with
4 tbsp/60 ml of water and cook until the tomatoes are pulpy.
Cover with a lid and continue cooking until the baby turnips have
softened.

3   Stir in the coriander, add the spinach and a little salt and pepper.
Cook for a further 2-3 minutes until the spinach has wilted.

4   Serve warm or cold.

Nutritional Highlights:

This recipe is beneficial for:

Acne
Digestion
Chronic Fatigue
Bad breath
Weight Loss

Each serve contains the
following RDA %'s:

Protein	23%
Vitamin A	479%
Vitamin C	211%
Vitamin E	46%
Vitamin K	1506%
Riboflavin	25%
Vitamin B6	32%
Folate	119%
Calcium	23%
Iron	36%
Magnesium	45%
Potassium	47%
Manganese	123%
Fiber	62%

Roasted Artichokes with Lemon Oil Dip

This is a very light and alkalising recipe ideal for these warmer days using charred artichokes.

Serves: 2
Preparation Time: 30 Minutes

Ingredients:
1 globe artichoke, trimmed
1/2 tbsp fresh lemon juice
6 garlic cloves, unpeeled
1/2 lemon (organic or unwaxed)
3 tbsp olive oil
Himalayan crystal salt or celtic sea salt
Freshly ground black pepper
Flat leaf parsley, to garnish

Instructions:

1 Preheat the oven to 200 Celsius (Gas 6). Add the lemon to a bowl of cold water. Cut each artichoke into wedges. Pull the hairy choke out from the centre, then put them into the acidulated water until needed.

2 Drain the artichoke wedges and place on a roasting tin with the garlic cloves. Add half the oil and mix well to coat. Sprinkle with salt and roast for about 40 minutes, stirring once or twice, until the wedges are tender and slightly charred.

3 Now, begin to prepare the dip. Using a sharp, small knife thinly pare away two strips of rind from the lemon. Lay the strips on a chopping board and scrape away any remaining pith. Place the rind in a small pan with water to cover. Bring to the boil and then simmer for about 5 minutes. Drain the rind, resfresh it in cold water and then chop it roughly. Set aside.

4 Arrange the cooked artichokes on a serving place and leave to cool for about 5 minutes. Gently flatten the garlic by using the back of a fork, so that the flesh squeezes out of the skins. Transfer the garlic flesh to a bowl, mash to a puree and then add the lemon rind. Squeeze the juice from the lemon and whisk it into the garlic mixture, together with the remaining oil.

5 Serve the artichokes warm with the lemon dip. Garnish with sprigs of flat leaf parsley and season to taste.

Nutritional Highlights:

This recipe is beneficial for:

Immune System
Acne
Digestion
Candida
Eczema

Each serve contains the following RDA %'s:

Vitamin A	24%
Vitamin C	64%
Vitamin E	15%
Vitamin K	314%
Vitamin B6	10%
Folate	17%
Iron	10%
Magnesium	10%
Manganese	16%
Fiber	19%

Kale Chickpea Mash
Mashing without Potatoes? Yes, you can!

Serves 2 as a main dish
Serves 4 as a side dish
Preparation Time: 20 Minutes

Ingredients:
3 tbsp garlic, cut into small pieces
1 shallot, cut into small pieces
1 bunch kale
400g fresh chickpeas (cooked pe
instructions)
2 tbsp Bragg Liquid Aminos
(alternative: soy sauce)
2 tbsp extra virgin olive oil or
coconut oil
1/2 tsp of fresh or dried thyme
Celtic sea salt or Himalayan
crystal salt, to taste

Instructions:

1 Gently fry the shallot and minced garlic in olive oil on medium-high heat until it turns golden brown. Be careful not to burn it, as the garlic becomes bitter tasting otherwise.

2 Add the washed and drained kale and stir in the oil, onion and garlic. After the kale has wilted a bit, add the chick peas and cook for about 6 minutes.

3 Add the remaining ingredients and stir. Begin mashing the chickpeas with a fork. You can mash them as fine as you like your mash to be.

Nutritional Highlights:

This recipe is beneficial for:

**Candida
Eczema
Colds & Flu
Digestion
Acne**

Each serve contains the
following RDA %'s:

Protein	26%
Vitamin A	158%
Vitamin C	125%
Vitamin E	10%
Vitamin K	521%
Thiamin	11%
Vitamin B6	65%
Calcium	17%
Iron	19%
Phosphorous	24%
Sodium	24%
Zinc	14%
Copper	27%
Manganese	96%
Fiber	39%

Courgettes with Moroccan Spices

Another favorite and easy to make dish from North Africa

Serves: 4
Preparation Time: 30 Minutes

Ingredients:
500g courgettes
Freshly squeezed lemon juice
from 1 lemon
Chopped fresh coriander and
parsley, to serve

For The Spicy Charmoula:
1 onion
1-2 garlic cloves, crushed
1/4 green or red chilli, seeded
and finely sliced
1/2 tsp paprika
1/2 tsp ground cumin
3 tbsp olive oil
Himalayan salt or celtic sea salt
Ground black pepper

Instructions:

1 Preheat the oven to 180C/Gas 4. Cut all the courgettes into quarters lengthways, and place in a shallow dish.

2 Finely chop the onion and blend with the other charmoula ingredients and 60ml/4 tbsp water. Pour over the courgettes. Cover and bake for 15 minutes.

3 Baste the courgettes with the charmoula, and return to the oven, uncovered, for 5-10 minutes until they are tender. Sprinkle with lemon juice and chopped herbs, and serve.

Tip: Use young courgettes with tender skin – older courgettes may need to be peeled.

Nutritional Highlights:

This recipe is beneficial for:

**Colds & Flu
Constipation
Libido
Blood Pressure
Osteoporosis**

Each serve contains the following RDA %'s:

Vitamin A	27%
Vitamin C	82%
Vitamin K	183%
Riboflavin	10%
Vitamin B6	20%
Folate	14%
Potassium	13%
Manganese	20%
Fiber	10%

Coconut Scented Rice with Toasted Almonds & Mint

Doing something a bit funky to make alkaline meals more enjoyable

Serves: 2
Preparation Time: 30 Minutes

Ingredients:
1 cup brown rice, rinsed
2 cups organic coconut milk
1/4 cup shredded coconut, optiona
1/4 cup almonds chopped finely
3 sprigs of fresh mint, finely
chopped

Instructions:

1 Preheat oven to 350 degrees F. Place rice, coconut milk and shredded coconut in a saucepan. Stir briefly.

2 Place saucepan over high heat and bring to a boil. Cover with a tight fitting lid then lower heat to a simmer. Cook rice for about 25 minutes. After that, check the rice periodically to see if it is tender.

3 While the rice is cooking, place the slivered almonds on a sheet pan and bake for 5-7 minutes or until toasty brown and fragrant.

When the rice is cooked to your desired tenderness, fluff it with a fork and sprinkle in about 1/2 the almonds. Add the rest of the almonds to the top of the rice, to serve along with the mint.

Nutritional Highlights:

This recipe is beneficial for:

Constipation
Thyroid
IBS
Candida
Libido

Each serve contains the following RDA %'s:

Protein	24%
Vitamin A	12%
Vitamin E	23%
Thiamin	13%
Riboflavin	13%
Niacin	19%
Vitamin B6	13%
Folate	16%
Calcium	12%
Iron	33%
Magnesium	48%
Potassium	26%
Manganese	192%
Selenium	22%
Fiber	37%

Chickpea and Avocado Mash
The perfect alkaline snack - protein, omega oils and greens!

Serves: 2-3
Preparation Time: 20 Minutes

Ingredients:
1 can chickpeas, drained or equivalent weight of organic dried chickpeas (garbanzos) cooked as per guidelines
1 ripe avocado
Handful of spinach leaves
Himalayan salt & cracked black pepper
Drizzle of flax oil
Pinch of cumin
Optional: herbs of your choice – coriander, basil, parsley

Instructions:

1 In a bowl, mix together chickpeas, avocado chunks, salt & pepper along with the cumin and the optional herbs. With a potato masher or large fork, mash together leaving some whole chickpeas.

2 Drizzle with the flax oil, add a dusting of paprika if you like it fancy and serve with the spinach, also drizzled in oil!

3 Optional: You can also put this in veggie & salad wraps – gives it more substance.

Nutritional Highlights:

This recipe is beneficial for:

Heart Health
Immune System
Acne
Digestion
PMS

Each serve contains the following RDA %'s:

Protein	19%
Vitamin A	97%
Vitamin C	48%
Vitamin E	16%
Vitamin K	329%
Thiamin	10%
Vitamin B6	47%
Folate	65%
Iron	20%
Magnesium	26%
Potassium	22%
Sodium	15%
Manganese	66%
Fiber	53%

Broccoli with Tahini

Rich in Vitamin C - Highly Satisfying!

Serves: 2
Preparation Time: 20-30 Minutes

Ingredients:
For the salad:
2-4 heads broccoli (use the florets only, not the stalk)
4 medium carrots

For the sauce:
125ml tahini
40ml olive oil
150ml water
50ml lemon juice
1½tsp ground coriander
¾tsp cumin
1/3tsp chilli pepper
1 tsp of sesame seeds
Lime slices for garnish and to squeeze

Instructions:

1 Remove the main pieces of stem from the broccoli, and then chop any remaining large pieces of stem off the florets. Separate the florets, if necessary, with the knife so that you end up with small 1-2cm pieces of broccoli. Put the florets into a large mixing bowl.

2 Now you can either take the option of having this as a RAW meal or lightly cooked. If you're going the cooking option I recommend either steaming for 2-3 minutes or rapidly 'steam-frying' for 2 minutes in a frying pan. This is just to make the broccoli slightly tender, rather than soft. You still want a crunch!

3 Grate the carrot and add to the mixing bowl.

4 Make the sauce by putting all of the sauce ingredients apart from the water and sesame seeds into a mini processor. Add about half the water and process. Then gradually add more water until you have a sauce that is gloopy and thick – the amount of water needed with depend on the consistency of your tahini. Add the sesame seeds and put to one side.

5 Pour the sauce over the top of all the ingredients and mix thoroughly.

6 Serve with a slice/quarter of lime, optional brown rice or a big salad.

Nutritional Highlights:

This recipe is beneficial for:

Heart Health
Immune System
Acne
Digestion
Loss

Each serve contains the following RDA %'s:

Protein	32%
Vitamin A	426%
Vitamin C	262%
Vitamin K	211%
Thiamin	61%
Riboflavin	31%
Niacin	17%
Vitamin B6	22%
Folate	24%
Calcium	32%
Magnesium	24%
Potassium	26%
Manganese	23%
Fiber	41%

Snacks

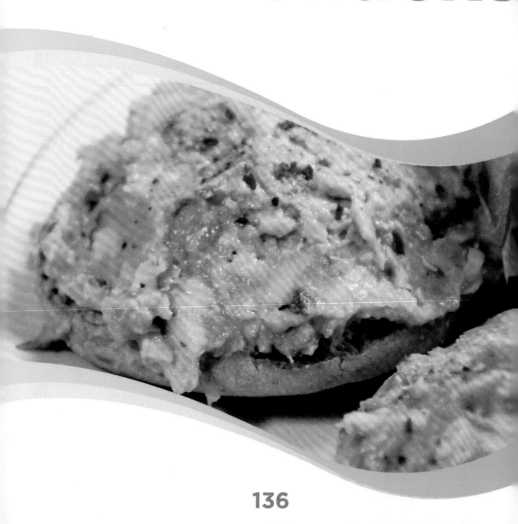

Alkaline Open Sandwich

The perfect, super-fast snack!

Serves: 2
Preparation Time: 5 Minutes

Ingredients:
2 slices of 'healthy' bread (see below)
1/2 avocado
1 handful of fresh basil
1 handful of fresh parsley
1 handful of rocket leaves
1/2 cucumber (80g)
1 tomato (90g)
2 tablespoons of alfalfa sprouts
Drizzle of olive oil
Pinch of Himalayan salt and black pepper

Instructions:

1 Start by washing and chopping the herbs and mixing together.

2 Next, scoop out the avocado and spread over the two slices of bread (remember, this recipe makes two open sandwiches).

3 Now slice the cucumber and place on the avocado, followed by the tomato.

4 Top with the herbs, rocket and alfalfa sprouts and drizzle with olive oil and sprinkle over a pinch of salt and freshly cracked black pepper.

Note on 'Healthy Bread': when I refer to 'healthy' breads and wraps I am meaning anything other than plain white or wholemeal. Aim, ideally, for sprouted breads, but any dark rye, spelt or gluten free is fine.

Nutritional Highlights:

This recipe is beneficial for:

Immune System
Acne
Candida
Eczema
Colds & Flu

Each serve contains the following RDA %'s:

Protein	13%
Vitamin A	75%
Vitamin C	73%
Vitamin K	177%
Thiamin	10%
Vitamin B6	15%
Folate	38%
Pantothenic Acid	11%
Calcium	14%
Iron	18%
Magnesium	12%
Phosphorous	11%
Potassium	22%
Manganese	35%
Fiber	29%

Soaked Almonds

The perfect omega snack

Serves: 1
Preparation Time: Overnight

Ingredients:
Raw, untreated almonds
Filtered, preferably ionised water

Instructions:

1 Simply soak the almonds so they are completely covered, in an airtight container, in the fridge overnight.

2 The next day they will be plump and delicious and the nutrients will be more bioavailable.

Nutritional Highlights:

This recipe is beneficial for:

Hearth Health
Immune System
Cholesterol
Osteoporosis
Chronic Fatigue
Brain Health

Each serve contains the following RDA %'s:

Protein	61%
Vitamin E	187%
Riboflavin	85%
Niacin	24%
Thiamin	20%
Folate	18%
Vitamin B6	10%
Manganese	163%
Magnesium	96%
Calcium	38%
Iron	30%
Potassium	29%
Zinc	29%
Fiber	70%

Nut Chips

Healthy, omega-oil-rich and spicy chips!

Serves: 2
Preparation Time: 1 Hour 10
Minutes

Ingredients:
1 cup of pecan nuts
1/2 cup of sunflower seeds
1/4 cup of pumpkin seeds
1 tsp cayenne pepper
1 pinch of chilli powder
Olive or coconut oil (use
whichever flavour you prefer)
Optional: 1/2 teaspoon of 'BBQ
Seasoning'
Himalayan salt & pepper to taste

Instructions:

1 Start by soaking all of the nuts and seeds for 1 hour.

2 Once soaked, rinse and drain the nuts and seeds and blend until with the spices and seasoning until coarse, but only just.

3 Mould into thin 'chips' / crackers and pad down to make solid.

4 Lightly pan fry on a low heat until golden on both sides.

Nutritional Highlights:

This recipe is beneficial for:

Heart Health
Immune System
Energy
Weight Loss
Bloating

Each serve contains the
following RDA %'s:

Protein	22%
Vitamin E	23%
Vitamin K	13%
Thiamin	14%
Riboflavin	10%
Vitamin B6	15%
Folate	12%
Iron	25%
Magnesium	47%
Phosphorous	41%
Potassium	12%
Zinc	27%
Manganese	149%
Selenium	13%
Fiber	26%

Vegetable Sticks

Raw and crunchy snack attack

Serves: 2
Preparation Time: 10 minutes
Ingredients:

1 Carrot
1 Capsicum (Bell Pepper)
1/2 Stick of Celery
1/2 Celeriac
1/2 Beetroot

Instructions:

1 Slice up into sticks and serve with any of the dips in this recipe book!

Nutritional Highlights:

This recipe is beneficial for:

Heart Health
Immune System
Energy
Weight Loss
Bloating

Each serve contains the following RDA %'s:

Protein	7%
Vitamin A	283%
Vitamin C	266%
Vitamin K	32%
Vitamin B6	21%
Folate	40%
Potassium	21%
Manganese	24%
Dietary Fibre	29%

Avocado on "Toast"

The perfect snack that you can make a million different ways

Serves: 2
Preparation Time: 10 Minutes

Ingredients:
2 slices of sprouted bread
1 avocado
Himalayan salt
Black pepper
Olive oil
Lemon juice

Optional:
Tomato
Rocket
Spinach
Sesame seeds
Or anything else!

Instructions:

1 Lightly toast the sprouted bread (or the healthiest bread you can find) and then spread on the avocado.

2 Now season with salt and pepper, drizzle on some olive oil and lemon juice.

3 Optional toppings can also be added to mix it up. I personally love a little rocket, sesame seeds and tomato.

Nutritional Highlights:

This recipe is beneficial for:

Colds & Flu
Constipation
Libido
Blood Pressure
Osteoporosis

Each serve contains the following RDA %'s:

Protein	16%
Vitamin C	69%
Vitamin K	73%
Vitamin B6	34%
Folate	49%
Pantothenic Acid	28%
Potassium	28%
Manganese	48%
Fiber	64%

Sauces, Dips & Dressings

Carrot Dip

Simple but alkalising dip to use with any snack, wrap or veggies

Serves: 2
Preparation Time: 15 Minutes

Ingredients:
1 carrot
1 tablespoon of fresh mint
1cm piece of fresh ginger
2 tablespoons of soy yoghurt
50ml orange juice
50 ml lemon juice

Instructions:

1 Grate the carrot and cook in a small saucepan with the fruit juice until the juice has evaporated and been absorbed. Now stand and let cool for 10 minutes.

2 Grate the ginger, or press in a garlic crusher.

3 Blend this mixture with the remaining ingredients.

Nutritional Highlights:

This recipe is beneficial for:

Acne
Digestion
Candida
Blood Cholesterol
Osteoporosis

Each serve contains the following RDA %'s:

Vitamin A	108%
Vitamin C	51%
Vitamin K	5%
Calcium	4%
Potassium	4%
Manganese	6%
Fiber	4%

Baby Pea and Broad Bean Spread

Fresh, textured and very easy to make spread to have as a snack or a side

Serves: 2
Preparation Time: 10 Minutes

Ingredients:
2 cups peas (fresh or frozen is fine)
1 cup of broad beans (fresh or frozen is fine)
1/3 avocado
1 clove of garlic
1/3 cup flax oil or olive oil
Himalayan or Celtic Sea Salt to taste (I usually use about 1/2 teaspoon)
A handful of fresh mint
3 sprigs of coriander
1 lemon, juiced and the rind of half of the lemon

Instructions:

1 Wash the peas and broad beans and put onto a light boil for two minutes.

2 Once done, put them into a colander and give them a wash over with cold water.

3 Place into a blender/food processor with the avocado, garlic, oil, salt, mint, the rind and coriander. Blend until smooth or chunky depending on your preference.

4 Add a little of the lemon juice to suit your taste.

5 Serve on sprouted breads/crackers, as a dip with fresh veggies or however you please!

Nutritional Highlights:

This recipe is beneficial for:

Acne
Digestion
Chronic Fatigue
Bad Breath
Muscle Development

Each serve contains the following RDA %'s:

Protein	46%
Vitamin K	103%
Manganese	75%
Vitamin C	50%
Vitamin A	36%
Copper	36%
Potassium	35%
Fiber	11%
Omega 3	175
Omega 6	1,086

*Omega 3 and 6 in mg

Black Bean Hummous

Awesome alkaline twist on traditional hummus!

Serves: 2
Preparation Time: 10 Minutes

Ingredients:
1 can black beans (200g), rinsed
and drained or 200g fresh/dried
black beans prepared
2 teaspoons fresh lemon juice
(or more to taste)
1 small handful of basil leaves
1 clove of garlic, crushed
1 large pinch of sesame seeds
Optional: red chilli to taste

Instructions:

1 In a food processor, process black beans, lemon juice, basil,
sesame seeds and garlic until thick. If it's too thick, you can add a
little water or tahini (if you have it).

Use as a dip, a spread in wraps, as a side to the Alkaline Fajitas
in my Alkaline Diet Recipe Book or in any way you like!

Nutritional Highlights:

This recipe is beneficial for:

Kidneys
Liver
Energy
Weight Loss
Bloating
Muscle Development

Each serve contains the
following RDA %'s:

Protein	49%
Vitamin K	80%
Thiamin	66%
Riboflavin	11%
Niacin	13%
Vitamin B6	23%
Folate	114%
Calcium	28%
Iron	41%
Magnesium	56%
Potassium	41%
Manganese	81%
Vitamin C	25%
Vitamin A	15%
Fibre	68%

Eastern Pesto!

Exciting Oriental twist on pesto - goes great with tofu and stir fry

Serves: 2
Preparation Time: 10 Minutes

Ingredients:
1 small chilli
2 tbsp basil, chopped
2 tbsp coriander, chopped
2 tbsp mint, chopped
1 tbsp parsley, chopped
Splash of coconut, flax or olive oil
Himalayan salt and pepper

Instructions:

1 Deseed the chilli and blend all ingredients in a food processor until sauce-like but a little chunky.

Nutritional Highlights:

This recipe is beneficial for:

Acne
Digestion
Candida
Osteoporosis
Liver

Each serve contains the following RDA %'s:

Vitamin A	50%
Vitamin C	80%
Vitamin K	275%
Vitamin B6	6%
Folate	5%
Iron	5%
Potassium	5%
Manganese	13%
Fiber	5%

Smooth Avocado and Tofu Dip

Delicious, Easy to Make, and Very Alkaline! Perfect for Snacking.

Makes: 1 bowl
Preparation Time: 15 Minutes

Ingredients:
1 avocado
1/2 pack of silken tofu
1 large tomato
1 clove of garlic
1 small onion (try brown or red)
Some fresh parsley (if available, but not vital)
Freshly ground black pepper and Himalayan/sea salt

Instructions:

1 Easy – just peel and core the avocado, roughly chop the tofu, tomato, garlic and onion, rip up the parsley and throw it all into a blender and blend until smooth!

2 If you want to thin it out a little you can add a little olive or avocado oil and some filtered water until you get the consistency you like. Or you can have it thick and rich. You can also make it as chunky or smooth as you like by blending for less or more time!

Nutritional Highlights:

This recipe is beneficial for:

Acne
Digestion
Candida
Osteoporosis
Liver

Each serve contains the following RDA %'s:

Protein	19%
Vitamin A	37%
Vitamin C	68%
Vitamin K	320%
Thiamin	5%
Vitamin B6	20%
Folate	31%
Iron	12%
Phosphorous	13%
Potassium	23%
Copper	16%
Manganese	15%
Fiber	32%

Garlic 'Mayonnaise'

Light, alkaline mayonnaise that is similar to aioli

Serves: 2
Preparation Time: 5 Minutes

Ingredients:
3 garlic cloves
290g silken tofu
180ml olive oil
Himalayan salt & pepper

Instructions:

1 Blend the garlic and tofu in a food processor until smooth.

2 Gradually add the oil while blending until it is all well blended.

3 Season to taste.

Nutritional Highlights:

This recipe is beneficial for:

Liver
Skin & Acne

Each serve contains the
following RDA %'s:

Protein	20%
Vitamin E	59%
Vitamin K	62%
Calcium	6%
Phosphorous	12%
Sodium	6%
Copper	9%

Salsa Fresca

Simple, fresh and energising

Serves: 2
Preparation Time: 5 Minutes

Ingredients:
3/4 green pepper
3/4 yellow pepper
2 tomatoes
Handful of basil
Handful of coriander
1/2 lemon, juiced
1/2 tbsp coconut or olive oil

Instructions:

1 Finely chop the pepper, tomatoes, basil and coriander and place in a bowl and stir in the lemon juice and an extra drizzle of the olive oil.

Nutritional Highlights:

This recipe is beneficial for:

Heart Health
Immune System
Acne
Digestion
Eczema

Each serve contains the following RDA %'s:

Vitamin A	60%
Vitamin C	322%
Vitamin K	143%
Vitamin B6	16%
Folate	14%
Potassium	14%
Manganese	25%
Fiber	16%

Tomato & Basil Sauce

Works well with everything! Adds an extra serve of raw alkaline veggies to any meal!

Serves: 2
Preparation Time: 10 Minutes

Ingredients:
5 ripe tomatoes
Big handful of fresh basil
2 garlic cloves
3 tbsp olive oil
1/4 red onion
Himalayan salt and pepper

Instructions:

1 Wash and roughly chop the tomatoes and halve the garlic cloves and roughly chop the onion.

2 Blend all ingredients until desired consistency is reached

Nutritional Highlights:

This recipe is beneficial for:

Colds & Flu
Constipation
Libido
Blood Pressure
Osteoporosis

Each serve contains the following RDA %'s:

Protein	10%
Vitamin A	95%
Vitamin C	87%
Vitamin K	248%
Niacin	10%
Vitamin B6	19%
Folate	23%
Potassium	23%
Manganese	49%
Fiber	22%

Alkaline Asian Dressing

Give your salad an Oriental flavor with this tasty alkaline dressing!

Serves: 2
Preparation Time: 5 Minutes

Ingredients:
1 tbsp of fresh Coriander/Cilantro
1 tbsp fresh grated ginger
1 tbsp fresh minced garlic
1 tbsp Bragg Liquid Aminos
1 tbsp fresh lemon juice
4 tbsp Udo's Choice or flax oil
1 tsp Sesame Seeds

Instructions:

1   Simply mix the ingredients well in a bowl or blender and whisk or
    blend until it's all combined and ready.

Nutritional Highlights:

This recipe is beneficial for:

Liver

Each serve contains the
following RDA %'s:

Vitamin K	27%
Vitamin A	10%
Vitamin C	12%
Vitamin E	19%
Vitamin B6	3%
Manganese	6%

Alkaline French Dressing

Instantly adds flavor to your salad - tangy and bursting with alkaline goodness!

Serves: 2
Preparation Time: 5 Minutes

Ingredients:
1/2 teaspoon of orange rind
1/2 teaspoon of lemon rind
Juice of 1 orange
Juice of 1 lemon
Slug of organic olive oil
2 tsp mustard
2 tbsp of mixed fresh parsley,
chives & tarragon (or any herbs
you like)
Himalayan salt & fresh pepper

Instructions:

1 All you need is a jar! Squeeze the fruit juices in and add the other ingredients and shake!

2 Keep refrigerated.

Nutritional Highlights:

This recipe is beneficial for:

Acne
Digestion
Candida
Cholesterol
Osteoporosis

Each serve contains the
following RDA %'s:

Protein	2%
Vitamin K	287%
Vitamin C	98%
Vitamin A	24%
Folate	9%
Thiamin	3%
Iron	5%
Potassium	5%
Calcium	2%
Dietary Fiber	3%

Coriander, Mint and Chilli Dressing

Perfect dressing for your alkaline snacks!

Serves: 2
Preparation Time: 5 Minutes

Ingredients:
1/2 small red onion
1 red chilli
1/2 cup of coconut yoghurt or
soya yoghurt
1 tbsp chopped fresh mint
1 tbsp chopped fresh coriander/
cilantro

Instructions:

1 Finely dice the onion and dice and deseed the chili
(or not if you like it hot!)

2 Mix the onion, chili with the yoghurt, mint and coriander

3 Put in the fridge for 1 hour to chill and infuse

Nutritional Highlights:

This recipe is beneficial for:

**Acne
Digestion
Candida
Colds & Flu
Bad Breath**

Each serve contains the
following RDA %'s:

Vitamin A	20%
Vitamin C	77%
Vitamin D	8%
Vitamin K	31%
Vitamin B6	9%
Calcium	10%
Manganese	11%

Red Pepper, Walnut, and Almond Omega Spread

A great dip that packs a huge hit of Omega 3!

Serves: 1-2
Preparation Time: 15 Minutes

Ingredients:
1 Red Bell Pepper/Capsicum
1/4 Cup of Walnuts
1/4 Cup of Almonds
50g Ground Flaxseeds/meal
1/2 Tbsp of Olive Oil
1/2 Tbsp of Flax Oil
1/2 Tsp of Ground Cumin
Himalayan Salt &
Coarse Black Pepper

Instructions:

1 Start by grilling your red pepper until it is blackened so you can peel away the skin. Next, if you have regular flax you need to grind it in a pestle and mortar or in a coffee bean grinder.

2 Now add the pepper, drained almonds, walnuts, flax, oils and cumin to a blender and pulse it until smooth. If more moisture is needed add a little extra olive oil or flax oil.

3 Season to taste and enjoy!

TIP: The prep for this recipe starts the night before by soaking the almonds.

Nutritional Highlights:

This recipe is beneficial for:

PMS
Kidney
Liver
Osteoporosis
Acne

Each serve contains the following RDA %'s:

Protein	24%
Vitamin A	38%
Vitamin C	127%
Vitamin E	28%
Thiamin	36%
Riboflavin	15%
Vitamin B6	14%
Folate	13%
Magnesium	44%
Phosphorous	28%
Copper	35%
Manganese	81%
Fiber	46%

Tahini and Lemon Dressing

Delicious and easy to make - great for your green salads!

Serves: 2
Preparation Time: 5 Minutes

Ingredients:
4 tbsp tahini
(bought or homemade)
4tbsp water
2 tbsp flax or olive oil
180ml lemon juice
2 tsp grated fresh ginger

Instructions:

1   Mix the water and tahini to make a smooth liquid, watering down the tahini.

2   Add the remaining ingredients and whisk!

Nutritional Highlights:

This recipe is beneficial for:

Immune System
Digestion
Candida
Eczema
Blood Pressure

Each serve contains the following RDA %'s:

Protein	11%
Vitamin C	72%
Vitamin E	12%
Thiamin	26%
Riboflavin	10%
Calcium	12%
Phosphorous	22%
Zinc	10%
Copper	24%
Manganese	22%
Fiber	13%

This Is Not The End!

I truly hope that this recipe book has provided you with the inspiration and enthusiasm to make the alkaline diet a permanent part of your lifestyle.

I thoroughly enjoyed creating this collection and these recipes have all played a big part in my diet over the past eleven years.

BUT...as you might have already seen or heard, my site, liveenergized.com is packed full of free guides, resources, videos and teaching, all aimed at helping you nourish your body, and make it easy, enjoyable and achievable to get to the health, vitality and body of your dreams...the health you deserve!

What's Next?

This is just the beginning! No matter where you are on your health journey, I strongly recommend you head over to www.liveenergized.com and immerse yourself!

You'll find more delicious recipes, guides, hundreds of video tutorials, plus access to:

 - The Alkaline Starter Guide (including 2x workbooks and 3 videos)
 - The Definitive Guide to Alkaline Water
 - The Complete Acid/Alkaline Food Chart

Plus so much more! There are literally over a thousand guides, articles and resources for you, all completely for free. Plus, you can contact me directly and get onto one of my frequent Q&A Coaching Calls (Webinars) and talk to me direct!

Until then, stay alkaline
Ross

Praise for The Alkaline Diet Recipe Books

"I LOVE THIS BOOK! The fresh, easy, delicious receipes and beautiful photos make it a joy to use and an inspiration to anyone wanting to improve their health and vitality with the alkaline diet.

Really inspiring and exactly what's needed!

I'm sure it will inspire many people and I'm so pleased to have my copy!"

Rose Elliot, MBE
Best-Selling Author of 3.5 million cookbooks and Briatin's favourite vegetarian chef.

"The Alkaline Diet Recipe Book is an inspiring "how to" manual for fun and tasty, genuinely healthy eating. This book is packed with tasty, nutrious and inspiring menu plans that are quick and easy to make. Ross's enthusiasm for the subject shines through in every page. If you're serious about your health, download or buy it ..... now!

I'll definitely be recommending this book to my patients. It should make my job as a pH, food focused nutritional therapist a lot easier!"

Gareth Edwards, BSc. DiplON. mBANT
www.food-for-life.co.uk

"It's like I've found the instruction manual for my body! I've lost 30kg in five months and I've got more energy, I'm happier and more confident. I love how good the food tastes and the variety your recipes bring.

Your recipes have increased my health & energy massively!"

Review by Daniel, Australia

"I bought this recipe book to help with my reflux and can now say...I have no more reflux! The recipes are delicious and really easy to make and I have now also lost 20kg!"

Review by Genevieve, USA

"Buying this book was the best thing I have ever done. My energy has increased 100% and from following the recipes I have clearer skin, better digestion, and I've lost 10.5kg!

The recipe book is full of real, healthy, filling and tasty foods!"

Review by Deanne, Australia

"I bought the book for Type II Diabetes and my blood sugar levels have now dropped from 23 to 06 and my weight has dropped by 9kg from 83kg to 74kg. Ankle pains, knees and joint pains have all gone.

When it comes to the recipes, the preparation and cooking times are unbelievable – I can't believe how fast and easy it is to cook Ross' recipes. My over all health improvement is fantastic and I say thanks to Ross. "

Review by Oliver, UK